Structural Performance of Col

Abdul Rashid Dar

Structural Performance of Cold-Formed Steel Composite Beams

LAP LAMBERT Academic Publishing

Imprint

Any brand names and product names mentioned in this book are subject to trademark, brand or patent protection and are trademarks or registered trademarks of their respective holders. The use of brand names, product names, common names, trade names, product descriptions etc. even without a particular marking in this work is in no way to be construed to mean that such names may be regarded as unrestricted in respect of trademark and brand protection legislation and could thus be used by anyone.

Cover image: www.ingimage.com

Publisher:
LAP LAMBERT Academic Publishing
is a trademark of
International Book Market Service Ltd., member of OmniScriptum Publishing Group
17 Meldrum Street, Beau Bassin 71504, Mauritius

Printed at: see last page
ISBN: 978-613-9-45256-9

Zugl. / Approved by: National Institute of Technology,Srinagar, J &K, Dissertation -2015

Structural Performance of
COLD-FORMED STEEL
COMPOSITE BEAMS
(Through Detailed Experimental Study)

Abdul Rashid Dar

1

Dedicated
to
Everyone

Who is Committed to Build

Safe & Eco-friendly Built-Environment

Preface

Primarily because of its unique structural properties, steel is still the only choice as an ideal material for construction of most of the challenging structures. Furthermore, steel is also the most suitable reinforcing material for concrete to overcome its inherent weakness, thus has transformed it into highly versatile construction material. This versatility leverage of concrete over other materials is the main reason for making it the most commonly used construction material. Keeping in view the above mentioned tremendous importance of steel in the construction industry as well as its limited reserves, there is a pressing need for ensuring its utmost economical utilization so that such a crucial construction material remains available for the benefit of mankind as long as possible. Accordingly, India, like other major countries, has also taken up a prestigious project called "Steel Economy Project" with a sole purpose of achieving most economical use of steel in the construction industry. In spite of lacking its potential for achieving the highest economy together with its limited choice of available cross sections, the hot-rolled steel members have been recognized as the most popular and widely used steel group in construction industry. No doubt the vital load resisting members in every structure need to have adequate safety to avoid their catastrophic collapse, hence use of hot rolled steel sections for such members can be justified because of their much better performance against premature buckling. However use of such sections for moderate to lightly loaded structural components (like flooring, roofing and similar other systems etc) generally remain under-utilized and thus contributes to substantial wasteful use of such a precious material with limited reserves. Cold Formed Steel (CFS), relatively a new steel group, provides an ideal choice to avoid such a wasteful use of steel. This steel group has not only great potential for achieving highest economy but also permits unlimited variety of shapes, thus making this type of steel construction as adaptable as reinforced concrete in its versatile use. Furthermore, like other developing countries, structural designers in India, are also faced with global competition in the design of fast track and cost effective structural systems to meet the huge deficit of various infrastructural systems necessary for bringing the country at par with global standards. For this purpose, CFS sections provide the best choice not only for cost effective structural systems (as mentioned above) but also an ideal choice for the desired fast track construction.

Since the individual components of CFS members are thin with respect to their widths, therefore the structural behavior of CFS members characterized by multiple premature buckling modes is not yet fully understood. Therefore, understanding the behavior of CFS members to avoid such premature buckling modes is one of the challenging problems in structural engineering which needs to be addressed with innovative solutions.

Flexural members are primary members in most of the structures and the sectional profiles given in the relevant CFS code does neither cover the variety of other efficient sectional profiles nor include other innovative techniques which may prove structurally much more efficient and highly economical as well. Hence there is an urgent need in the CFS industry not only to look beyond the conventional CFS beam sections but also explore other innovative options such as appropriate stiffening arrangements and other similar solutions with great potential in avoiding undesirable premature buckling modes of failure in CFS beams. Accordingly, this book presents the extensive experimental study to investigate several innovative options, particularly in terms of varying composite beams using low cost lightweight packing materials as well as some novel stiffening arrangements applicable to CFS flexural members for their best structural performance. The partial stiffening of the flange lip has greatly contributed towards the improvement in both strength as well as stiffness characteristics, which confirms the important role of appropriate partial stiffening in improving the structural performance of CFS beam sections. The timber planks firmly connected to the conventional CFS lipped I section has drastically improved the load carrying capacity. It is worth highlighting here that the load carrying capacity of steel angle stiffened model and the timber stiffened model are comparable. However the strength to weight ratio of the timber stiffened model is considerably higher than that of steel angle stiffened model, thus validating much better steel economy achieved in timber stiffened model which is highly encouraging.

This book will be very useful for researchers, academicians, students etc. as well as for professionals like, design consultants, architects, site engineers, builders etc.

Abdul Rashid Dar
N I T Srinagar
Kashmir
e-mail: abdulrashid@nitsri.net

February, 2019

Preface

Contents

NOTATIONS

Abbreviations

AISI	= American Iron & Steel Institute
ANSI	= American National Standards Institute
AS 4100	= Australian Standard for the Design of Steel Structures
AS/NZ 4600	= Australian Standard for the Design of Cold Formed Steel Structures
ASD	= Allowable Stress Design
BM	= Bending Moment
BSI	= British Standard Institution
CFS	= Cold Formed Steel
CSA	= Canadian Standard Association
LRFD	= Load Resistance Factor Design Specification

Symbols

A	= Area of Cross-section
b	= Width of the flange
b_e	= Effective Width of Flat Plate
d_{min}	= Minimum Depth of Lip Required
E	= Modulus of Elasticity
E_s	= Modulus of Elasticity of Steel
E_w	= Modulus of Elasticity of Wood
f	= Applied Stress
f_b	= Basic Design Stress
$f_{cr,b}$	= Extreme Fibre Compressive Elastic Lateral Buckling Stress
f_{bd}	= Design Bending Compressive Stress Corresponding to Lateral Buckling

7

f_y = Yield Stress

I, I_{xx} or I_z = Moment of Inertia about Major Axis

I_{min} = Minimum Moment of Inertia of the edge Stiffener

k = Local Buckling Coefficient

K_4 = Timber Capacity Reduction Factor

L_{LT} = Effective Length

M = Member Moment Capacity

M_s = Nominal Section Moment Capacity

M_y = Yield Moment

p_1 = Design Coefficient

q_1 = Design Coefficient

t = Steel thickness

t_f = Thickness of Flange

t_w = Thickness of Web

Y = Distance of the Extreme Compression Fiber from the Neutral Axis

Z_e = Effective Sectional Modulus

Z, Z_f or Z_y = Full Sectional Modulus about Major Axis

Z_{pz} = Plastic Sectional Modulus about Major Axis

χ_{LT} = Strength Reduction Factor for Lateral Torsional Buckling of a beam

γ_1 = Design Coefficient

ρ = Effective Width Factor

λ or λ_{LT} = Non-dimensional Slenderness

ϕ_{LT} = Resistance Reduction Factor

ψ = Capacity Reduction Factor

Chapter-1

Introduction

1.1 General

Because of its unique structural properties, steel is the only choice as an ideal construction material for most of the challenging structures such as very long span bridges, very tall buildings etc. Further steel is also an ideal reinforcement for otherwise a non-versatile material like plain concrete (overcoming its inherent undesirable property of low tensile strength) thus making it one of the versatile construction materials, namely RCC, world over.

In view of the above referred key role played by steel in the modern construction industry, there is an urgent need to ensure the most economic utilization of this precious material for benefit of mankind not only at present but in future as well. For this purpose, like other countries India has also taken up an important project called "Steel Economy Project" with a sole purpose of achieving most economical use of steel in the construction industry. Steel members used for civil engineering construction fall under two groups.

- Hot-rolled steel members which are formed at elevated temperatures.
- Cold-Formed Steel (CFS) members which are formed at room temperatures.

Until recently, the hot rolled steel member have been the most popular and widely used steel group but lacks the potential for its optimum use especially in case of light to moderate loaded structures or structural components. On the other hand, CFS relatively a new steel group has great potential for economical use particularly for light to moderate loaded structures.

In contrast to hot rolling, with limited choice of hot rolled cross sectional profiles, the cold formed processes coupled with automatic welding permit an unlimited variety of shapes, thus making this type of steel construction not only highly economical but also as adoptable to special structural requirements as reinforced concrete in its versatile use. Furthermore, like other developing countries, structural designers in India, are faced with global competition in the design of fast track and cost effective structural systems to meet the huge deficit of various infrastructural systems. Such a development is crucial for bringing the country at par with global standards. For this purpose, CFS sections provide the best choice not only for cost effective structural systems (as mentioned above) but also an ideal choice for the desired fast track construction.

1.2 Judicious Use of Cold-Formed Steel

Having highlighted the most valuable and rewarding features of CFS sections, this group of steel however suffer from some potential structural limitations, notable among them being various buckling modes when used as compression or flexural members. Many of the cold formed shapes currently in use are given in IS-811 1987 (one of the series of Indian Standards being published under Steel Economy Project). The sectional profiles given in the code don't exhaust the variety of sections which may prove not only more efficient but economical as well. There is no doubt that innovativeness character of structural engineering will keep on producing new sectional profiles with much better structural performance, especially in terms of economy, than many of those given in the code. In the development of new innovative structural sections, the main aim has to be development of such shapes which on one hand greatly contribute to economical use of material (i.e. high strength to weight ratio) and on the other hand has desired versatility potential of mass production as well as ease in fabrication (i.e. allowing simple connection detailing to other structural members).

1.3 Motivation & Justification of Present Study

No doubt the main members in structures need to have adequate safety to avoid catastrophe/total collapse, hence use of hot rolled steel sections for such members may become necessity because of their much better performance against premature buckling However use of hot rolled steel sections for moderate to lightly loaded members such as floor beams, purlins, etc. generally remains under-utilized. This contributes to highly conservative use of such a precious construction material with limited reserves. Keeping in view the importance of steel as the most precious construction material, it is of paramount importance to make the most economical use of the same. CFS provides an ideal choice to avoid such a wasteful use of steel. Unlike hot rolling, the cold forming process permits an almost infinite variety of shapes to be produced which can serve desired needs efficiently. Since the individual components of CFS members are thin with respect to their widths, thus prone to premature buckling at compressive stress levels much lower than yield stress. Avoiding such premature buckling of CFS elements is therefore most challenging problem in CFS construction and needs to be addressed with innovative solutions.

Flexural members are the prime members in most of the structures. Since shape of beam cross section plays an important role, hence there is an urgent need to develop innovative beam sectional profiles that have inherent resistance to such premature buckling modes thus exhibiting better structural performance. Provision of appropriate stiffening arrangement also contributes greatly in avoiding premature buckling. Accordingly, the present study is mainly focused on experimental investigation of these important aspects of CFS flexural members.

1.4 Objectives

Because of several major limitations with hot rolled steel sections, which contribute to considerable wasteful use of steel in construction industry, urgent need has been realized for its appropriate replacement to overcome all such limitations. Further keeping in view the importance of steel as the precious construction material, the most economical use of the same is even more demanding. CFS provides an ideal choice for such desperately needed replacement with lot of potential to avoid wasteful use of steel. However, the individual components of CFS members are thin with respect to their widths, therefore the structural behavior of CFS members characterized by multiple premature buckling modes is the most challenging problem not yet fully understood. In order to promote the large scale use of CFS in construction industry with adequate confidence, this challenging premature buckling problem of CFS sections needs to be addressed with innovative solutions duly supported by experimental validation (Adil Dar M. et al., 2014). Such an approach will finally facilitate the development of standard design rules for safe design of CFS members necessary for promoting the desired large scale use of CFS in construction industry. In recent years, some research work has been carried out in this direction, but lot more needs to be done for achieving encouraging results. Accordingly, in the present work attempt has been made to address some of these premature buckling problems of CFS sections, particularly for flexural members, with following objectives:

- Considering the prominent role played by carefully chosen sectional profiles for achieving valuable inherent resistance against premature buckling modes, several varying sectional profiles have been proposed for detailed experimental study to investigate their contribution towards the desired inherent resistance against premature buckling.

- For successful achievement of considerable reduction in member self weight of CFS sections (necessary for achieving maximum strength to weight ratio), the use of thinner wall thickness in CFS sections is very essential. Accordingly, thinner steel sheets from 1mm to 2mm thick have been chosen for fabrication of varying beam sectional profiles. However, such low wall thickness sections become extremely vulnerable to multiple modes of premature buckling not yet fully understood. Providing of appropriate stiffening arrangement contributes considerably in avoiding premature buckling. Accordingly, various innovative stiffening/strengthening arrangements have been proposed for result oriented experimental study to evaluate their effectiveness for avoiding local buckling failure of thin walled sections before attaining overall failure. The various forms of stiffening arrangements to be attempted in this study may include:1) intermittent steel stiffeners within vulnerable zone of span, 2) continuous steel stiffeners covering full vulnerable zone of span, 3) continuous stiffeners using low cost materials covering entire span.

- For complex problems, when formulation of design formulas / analytical methods are not possible, then carefully performed experimental testing provides the best tool to make a valuable contribution in this direction. Due to non availability of design rules for innovative solutions proposed either in terms of new sectional profiles or in terms of innovative stiffening arrangements or both, it is rather impossible to predict with acceptable accuracy the modes of premature buckling in general and premature local buckling in particular. Meticulously performed experimental testing is of great help in not only identifying locations which are most vulnerable to premature local buckling but also help in knowing the most effective remedial/ stiffening measures necessary to arrest any such premature failure. Accordingly, identification of such locations together with knowing the most effective remedial/ stiffening measures necessary to arrest local premature buckling for beams with proposed innovative solutions has been another important objective of present experimental study. Once such remedial measures (if required) stands identified, then next important target of present study will be to assess experimentally the effectiveness of the proposed strengthening/remedial measures.

- Experimental validation of existing design rules for CFS beams will be of great help to structural designers to use such design rules with confidence. Therefore, experimental results obtained here shall be used for validation of the current design rules stipulated in national & international codes for various CFS beam sections, wherever applicable.

- In order to promote the use of CFS sections on a large scale, there is an urgent need to develop generalized design rules covering wide range of CFS sectional profiles conventional as well as innovative for safe design of CFS members in general and flexural members in particular. For this purpose a methodical and comprehensive parametric study using advanced analytical techniques like finite element modeling on one hand and high precision experimental investigation on the other hand will be required. Till such design rules become available, it may be attempted to use experimental results of present study to find suitable modification factors necessary for extension of existing design rules to other nonconventional sectional profiles proposed in this study.

1.5 Strategy & Methodology

The methodology to be adopted for achieving the various objectives is described as under:

- Shortlisting of analytically evaluated optimum sectional profiles for experimental validation
- Development of suitable testing facilities
- Fabrication of various innovative beam profiles for testing
- Selection of feasible packing materials.
- Selection of appropriate stiffening arrangements
- Detailed experimental testing of various beam models with varying geometry, stiffening arrangement /packing materials.
- Detailed analysis of experimental data followed by its interpretation and discussion.

1.6 Book Layout

The detailed investigations of flexural behaviour of innovative CFS beam sections using analytical methods (stipulated in codes) as well as extensive experimental testing with varying: i) sectional profiles (of different wall thickness), ii) low cost packing/ connecting materials and iii) appropriate stiffening arrangements are presented in this book in following seven chapters. The contents of each chapter are briefly described as under:

Chapter 1: This chapter presents remarkable advantages of cold-formed steel sections over conventional hot rolled steel sections followed by the judicious use of CFS, its research needs, objectives of the present study and the research methodology adopted.

Chapter 2: A summary of current literature relating to various aspects of cold- formed steel

13

flexural members, independent reading analyses of previous findings are presented in this chapter. Experimental and analytical investigations conducted by previous researchers are also described evaluating their findings and methods of testing.

Chapter 3: This chapter presents the special characteristics and design considerations of cold-formed steel members and various buckling modes of failure. Finally the description of design standards about CFS followed by Codal Design procedures (National & International) is also covered briefly.

Chapter 4: This chapter presents development of testing facility followed by selection of facility specific model parameters. Common and specific characteristics of various models are also presented. Finally analytical load carrying capacities of various models are worked out followed by fabrication of the selected models for experimental testing.

Chapter 5: This chapter describes the need for experimental investigation followed by loading & data recording arrangements adopted. Finally, detailed experimental testing of various models with specific characteristics and corresponding data collection of each model is presented.

Chapter 6: This chapter presents the data analysis including graph plotting. This is finally followed by meaningful interpretation and appropriate discussion about the promising results obtained.

Chapter 7: In this chapter, a summary of the most remarkable findings of this research is presented along with the recommendations for future research.

Chapter-2

Literature Review

2.1 Introduction

The use of CFS members in building construction began in the 1850s in both the United States and Great Britain. In the 1920s and 1930s, the acceptance of CFS as a construction material was still very limited because there was no standard design methodology available and CFS was not included in the building codes at that time. Many of the CFS applications were unable to be used due to the lack of design methodology and product recognition. To face this challenge, American Iron and Steel Institute (AISI) convened a technical committee in 1938, known as the Committee on Building Code, with the mission of developing a specification for the design of CFS structures. Research work was conducted at Cornell University, led by Professor George Winter. Eight years later, in 1946, the first Specification for the Design of Light Gauge Steel Structural Members was published, and in 1949, the first Design Manual was available for use by design engineers. In India the first edition of code of practice for use of cold-formed light gauge steel structural members in general building construction was first published by Indian Standard (IS) in 1975 (IS: 801 - 1975). The first edition of the Specification for the Design of Light Gage Steel Structural Members was published by the <u>American Iron and Steel Institute</u> (AISI) in 1946 (AISI, 1946). After ten years of mutual efforts, the first edition of the North American Specification for the Design of Cold – Formed Steel Structural Members was published in 2001.This document was immediately adopted by the International Building Code and was recognized by the American National Standards Institute (A.N.S.I.) as the National Standard in the United States.

2.2 Previous Research in CFS

Structural behaviour of the commonly used CFS sections has been well researched in the past. However, only limited research has been undertaken to investigate the structural performance of new and innovative CFS sectional profiles.

In the 1960's, under the School Construction Systems Development Project of California, four modular systems of school construction were developed by Inland Steel Production Company. These systems have been proven to be efficient structures at reduced cost. They are successful not only for school but also for industrial and commercial buildings throughout USA.

In 1970, Republic Steel Corporation was selected by the Department of Housing and Urban Development under the Operation Breakthrough Program to develop a modular system for housing.

In 2000, the 165 unit Holiday Inn in Federal Way, Washington, utilized eight stories of axial load bearing CFS studs as primary load bearing members.

2.3 Previous Research in CFS Flexural Members

The history of developments on CFS flexural members can be traced back to 1965 when O Connor et al. (1965) first showed that the inclusion of various closed cells to I- section beams improved their performance against buckling failure significantly. They found that this improvement of buckling behaviour was mainly due to increase in torsional rigidity. This led the researchers to focus on CFS sections with torsionally rigid flanges, which can delay or eliminate structural instability problems effectively which being the main cause for the premature failure of such members at much lower loading.

Zhao and Mahendran (2001) at Queensland University of Technology initiated a research program to investigate the structural behaviour and design of such torsionally rigid flange beam sections. Their study used rectangular hollow flanges and various manufacturing methods such as spot welding, self-pierced riveting and screw fastening to form torsionally rigid flange beam sections from a single steel strip. Their study has identified that the type of fastening and spacing does not affect the member compression capacity significantly. However, the structural behaviour and design of torsionally rigid flange beam as flexural members will be different and therefore further investigations are needed to identify their failure modes and develop suitable design rules for torsionally rigid flange beam as flexural members. Accordingly an attempt has been made in this research to study the flexural behaviour and design of CFS beams with innovative sectional profiles made of separately formed flanges and web connected by simple screw fastening.

M S Deepak et al. (2012) evaluated structural behavior of CFS lipped C channel beams due to lateral buckling of beams and load carrying capacity. It was seen that the decrease in d/t ratio shows increase in load carrying capacity. And also there is increase in deflection of beams. The failure of the beam is at the critical sections where the stresses are maximum at points of loading.

2.4 Failure of CFS Beams - A Case Study

During the concrete placement on the second story of a building under construction, the CFS beams supporting the decking and concrete collapsed. Four workers were injured, one fracturing his hip. Approximately two-thirds of the deck had been placed. The project structural engineer had been at the site earlier but had left before the collapse.

The collapse occurred while concrete was being placed onto steel decking on the second floor of the structure. The steel decking was supported by 203-mm deep CFS beams with 1.21-mm wall thickness without shoring. Some of the workers raised concerns about the safety of the structure with the project structural engineer. He assured the contractor and workers that shoring was unnecessary and that the beams were rated for more than enough capacity to support the concrete.

The testimony of the workers and the photographs available indicated that good construction practices were followed with respect to placing and finishing the concrete. The project structural engineer contended that the failure occurred because workers allowed the concrete to pile up on the formwork, thus increasing the load.

Immediately before the collapse, concrete was being placed from a pump onto the decking. An experienced worker was using the pump nozzle to spread the concrete. The workers started at one end, moving toward the other end of the second floor. One worker claimed that the deck was vibrating during the concrete placement.

When approximately two-thirds of the concrete had been placed, the decking on the longer 4-m span gave way suddenly, and five of the workers fell. Two workers were able to grab wire mesh and avoid falling the entire distance. The others fell onto the first floor.

Chapter-3

Special Characteristics & General Design Considerations

3.1 Introduction

Unlike conventional hot rolled steel members, there are certain unique characteristics related to CFS members, particularly due to their forming process and the use of thinner wall thickness. In CFS design, individual elements of CFS structural members are usually thin and the width to thickness ratios are large. These thin elements may buckle locally at a stress level much lower than the yield stress of steel when they are subjected to compression in flexural bending, axial compression, shear, or bearing. Since local buckling of individual elements of CFS sections has often been one of the major challenges, the design load should be so determined that adequate safety is provided against failure caused by local instability with due consideration given to the post-buckling strength(W.W. Yu & R.A. LaBoube, 2010).

3.2 Effect of Cold-forming

When steel shapes are cold-formed by either press-braking or cold-rolled-forming, there is a change in mechanical properties of the material due to cold working of the metal. Because the material properties undoubtedly play an important role in the performance of structural members, it is important they are included in the design of cold-formed sections. Macdonald et al. (1997) described that the yield strength, and to a lesser extent the ultimate strength, are increased and ductility is reduced as a result of this cold working, particularly in the bends of the section. Consequently, the material properties of a formed section may be markedly different from those of the virgin sheet material from which it is formed. The tests conducted by Karren and Winter (1967) illustrated the variation of mechanical properties from the parent material at the specific locations in a channel section as shown in Figure 1).

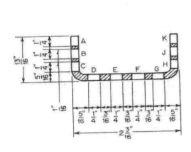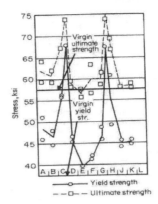

Figure1: Effect of Cold-work on Mechanical Properties in a Channel Section (KarrenandWinter,1967)

Hancock (1998) stated that there search investigations by, Karren (1967) and Chajes (1963) on the influence of cold working in steel Winter (1968) indicated that the changes of mechanical properties due to cold work are caused mainly by strain hardening and strain ageing as illustrated in Figure 2.

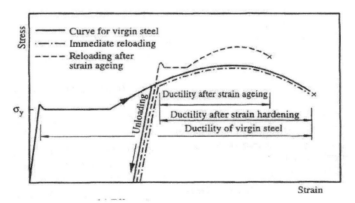

Figure2: Effect of Strain Hardening and Strain Aging on Stress-strain Characteristics (Chajesetal.,1963)

3.3 Special Design Criteria

A set of unique problems pertaining to CFS design has evolved mainly due to the thinner wall thickness and cold-forming process used in the production of cold-formed sections. Hence, unlike the usually

19

thicker conventional hot-rolled steel members, the design of CFS members must be given special considerations while designing such members. A brief summary of such considerations is listed next.

3.3.1 Local Buckling& Post Buckling Strength

Individual elements forming CFS members are usually thin with respect to their width. Therefore, they are likely to buckle at a lower stress than yield point when they are subjected to compression, bending, shear or bearing forces .However, unlike one-dimensional structural elements such as columns, stiffened compression elements will not collapse when the buckling stress is reached, but they of ten continue to carry increasing loads by means of redistribution of stresses (Winter,1970). The ability of these locally buckled elements to carry further load, known as post buckling strength, is allowed in the design to achieve an economic solution.

Local buckling has the significant undesirable effect on the load carrying capacity of columns and beams due to reduction in stiffness and strength of the locally buckled plate elements. Therefore it is highly desirable to avoid such local buckling before yielding of the member. Most of the hot rolled steel sections have enough wall thickness to eliminate local buckling before yielding. However, fabricated sections and thin walled CFS members usually experience local buckling of plate elements before the yield stress is reached.

It is useful to classify sections based on their tendency to buckle locally before overall failure of the member takes place. For those cross sections liable to buckle locally, special precautions need to be taken in design. However, it should be remembered that local buckling does not always spell disaster. Local buckling involves distortion of cross-section. There is no shift in the position of the cross-section as a whole as in global or overall buckling. In some cases, local buckling of one of the less important elements of the cross-section may be allowed since it does not adversely affect the performance of the member as a whole. In the context of plate buckling, it is pointed out that substantial reserve strength exists in plates beyond the point of elastic buckling. Utilization of this reserve capacity may prove very helpful in achieving the desired economic design

Figures 3(a) and (b) illustrate two cases of local buckling of thin-walled box and plate girders. The plates supported on three sides (outstands) have a buckling coefficient 'k' roughly one-tenth that for plates supported on all four sides (internal elements). Therefore, in open sections such as I-sections, the flanges which are outstands tend to buckle before the webs which are supported on all edges. Further, the entire length of the flanges is likely to buckle in the case of axially compressed member under consideration, in the form of waves. On the other hand, in closed sections such as hollow rectangular section, both flanges and webs behave as internal elements and the local buckling of the flanges and webs depends on their respective width-thickness ratios.

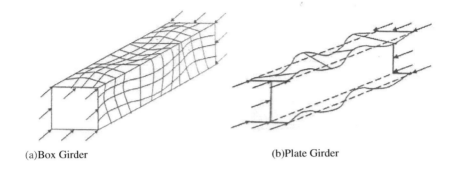

(a)Box Girder   (b)Plate Girder

Figure3: Local Buckling of Compression Flanges (SCI,1998)

3.3.2 Torsional Rigidity

Many of the steel shapes produced by cold-forming are mono symmetric open sections with their shear centre eccentric from their centroid as illustrated in Figure 4. The eccentricity of loads from the shear centre axis will generally produce considerable torsional deformation in the thin-walled beams as a result of flexural-torsional buckling . The torsional rigidity of an open section is proportional to t^3 (t, is member thickness) so that the cold-formed steel sections consisting of thin elements are relatively weak against torsion. Hence torsional stiffness of cold-formed steel members is an important criterion in the design of cold-formed steel sections to achieve an economic solution.

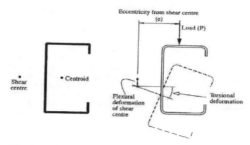

Figure4: Torsional Deformations in Eccentrically Loaded Channel Beam (Hancock,1998)

3.3.3 Distortional Buckling

Thin-walled flexural or compression members composed of high-strength steel and /or slender elements in the section, which are braced against lateral or flexural-torsional buckling, may under go a mode of buckling commonly called distortional buckling (Hancock,1997). The previous research studies (Ellifrittetal.,1992, Kavanaghand Ellifritt, 1993 and 1994) have shown that a discretely braced beam, not attached to deck and sheeting ,may fail either by lateral-torsional buckling between braces, or by distortional buckling at or near the braced point.

Two modes of distortional buckling are specified in the CFS design standard, AS/NZS 4600(SA,1996). The first one is flange distortional buckling, Which involves rotation of a flange and lip about the flange / web junction of a C-section or Z-section and the second one is lateral-distortional buckling, which involves transverse bending of vertical web (see Figures 5(a) and (b)). Flange distortional buckling is most likely to occur in the open thin-walled sections such as C-sections and Z-sections while lateral–distortional buckling is the most likely in beams, such as hollow flange beams, where the high torsional rigidity of the tubular compression flange prevents it from twisting during lateral displacement (Piand Trahair, 1997). The distortional buckling concept is first introduced into AS/NZS 4600 in its 1996 version (SA,1998).

(a) Distortional Buckling   (b)Lateral Distortional Buckling

Figure5: Buckling of a Channel Section and a Hollow Flange Beam (SA,1998)

3.4 CFS Design Standards

Specifications and standards for the design of CFS structural members are available in many countries. The design clauses for CFS structural members were first introduced with the preparation of the American Iron and Steel Institute Specifications in 1946, using the research work on cold-formed members of Professor George Winterat Cornell University (AISI,1946). The British Steel Standard, BS 449(BSI,1959) was modified in 1961 to include the design of cold-formed members by the inclusion of Addendum No.1(1961) based on the work of Professor A.H.Chilver (BSI,1961). In Australia, the Australian Standard for the design of CFS structural members, AS 1538 (SAA,1974) was first published in 1974. It was based mainly on the 1968 edition of the American Specifications but with some modifications to the beam and column design curves to keep the maligned with the Australian Steel Structures Code ASCA1-1968 (SAA, 1968).

In Australia, a significant revision of the 1974 edition of AS1538 was produced using the 1980 and 1986 editions of the American Iron and Steel Institute Specification (AISI, 1980 and 1986) in 1988. However, they were all in an allowable (permissible) stress format (ASD). In India the first edition of code of practice for use of cold-formed light gauge steel structural members in general building construction was first published by Indian Standard (IS) in 1975 (IS: 801 – 1975). The American Iron and Steel Institute produced a limit state version of their 1986 specification in 1991, called the Load and Resistance Factor Design Specification (LRFD) (AISI, 1991). In 1990, Standards Australia published the limit stated sign standard for steel structures called AS4100 based on the load factor and capacity factor approach similar to that used for LRFD in the USA. In 1993, Standards Australia and Standards New Zealand commenced work on a limit states design standard for cold-formed steel structures to suit both countries (SA, 1996). The new standard called AS/NZS 4600 is based mainly on the latest AISI specifications (AISI, 1996). In the UK, BS5950, Part 5 is the principal source of guidance for the design of cold-formed structural steel work (BSI, 1998). Other international standards for CFS structures which are in a limit state format include, the Eurocode3 EC3 (ENV, 1996) and the Canadian Standard CAN/CSA S136-94 (CSA, 1994).

3.5 Current Design Methods

In India the first edition of code of practice for use of cold-formed light gauge steel structural members in general building construction was first published by Bureau of Indian Standard (BIS) in 1975

(IS: 801- 1975). This code is based on working stress method. There are no amendments to this code. Moreover it is not revised to the latest research findings. There are no guidelines for hollow flanged sections. This code is used in the next chapter for analysis and designing of models.

Standards of Australia, Draft for Cold formed steel structures, AS/NZS 4600 : 2005 is the revised code based on latest research findings. This code is based on limit state design. This code is used in the next chapter for analysis and designing of models.

3.6 National & International Codal Design Procedures

Design Steps as per IS-801(1975)

I)   Computation of effective width

Basic Design Stress(f_b)= $0.6f_y$

$$\text{For (b/t) upto (b/t)}_{lim}= 446/\sqrt{f}, \text{ b=w}$$

$$\text{For (b/t)} > \text{(b/t)}_{lim,} , \text{(b/t)}= \frac{658}{\sqrt{f}} \ (1- \frac{145}{(b/t)\sqrt{f}})$$

II)   Determination of Moment of Inertia & Sectional Modulus

$$I=bd^3/12 + A\hat{Y}^2$$

$$Z= I/Y$$

III) Determination of Safe Load

$$M=fZ$$

Design Steps as per AS/NZ 4600

I)   Determination of Centroid, Moment of Inertia. & Sectional Modulus.

II)   Determination of Section Moment Capacity(M_y)

$$M_y=Z_f f_y$$

III) **Determination of Effective Widths of Elements**

$$b_e = \rho b$$

$$\rho = \frac{(1 - \frac{0.22}{\lambda})}{\lambda} < 1.0$$

$$\lambda = \left[\frac{1.052}{(\sqrt{k})}\right](b/t)\sqrt{\frac{f}{E}}$$

IV) **Determination of Centroid, Moment of Inertia. & Sectional Modulus of the Effective Section.**

V) **Determination of Section Moment Capacity of the Effective Section**

$$M_s = Z_e f_y$$

Chapter-4

Design & Fabrication of Beam Models

4.1 General

For high quality experimental work, it is very essential to have standard testing facilities and high precision measuring instrumentation. This chapter presents the development of experimental set up, particularly the important details of 500kN capacity Testing Rig ideal for performing high quality experimental testing on beams. This chapter also describes the important common as well as specific characteristics of various testing models followed by their theoretical design and fabrication.

4.2 Development of Experimental Setup

For carrying out testing on beam models, a 500kN capacity Testing Rig as shown in Figure 6, was developed to meet the requirements for high precision beam testing. Following are the salient features of the Testing Rig.

A beam up-to a maximum span of 7.5m,a maximum depth of 250mm and a maximum width of 300mm can be tested.

A hydraulic jack of 500kN capacity along with high precision 100kN capacity proving ring was used for load application on models.

Suitable arrangement was made for application of Two Point Loading as seen in

Figure6.

The heavy supporting frames allow easy mounting of beam models along with ideal arrangement for placement of dial gauges as seen in Figure 6 .

Proper arrangement was made to simulate simple support conditions for beam models.

High precision Dial Gauges of 50mm travel were used to measure the deflections at three vital locations.

Figure6: 500kN Capacity Testing Rig for Beams.

4.3 Testing Facility Governed Model Parameters

Constraints with the Testing Rig cited above govern the following basic model parameters.

Space available on either side of Testing Rig governs span of the beam test Models.

Vertical clearance available within the Testing Rig controls depth parameter of the beam Models.

Horizontal clearance available within the Testing Rig governs width parameter of the Models.

4.4 Constant Characteristics of All Models

To have successful achievement of various objectives of the project, eleven models with judiciously proposed specific variations in terms of sectional geometry, appropriate packing materials and effective stiffening arrangements have been chosen for detailed experimental testing. To make the contribution of each specific variation towards favourable structural response prominently noticeable in experimental measurements, it was of paramount importance to ensure strict uniformity of all such parameters, not forming part of current studies, but to which the targeted experimental measurements are highly sensitive. These include span of the beam, support conditions, location of applied point loads and bearing/stiffening arrangement under concentrated applied load/reaction points. Accordingly, all such sensitive parameters kept strictly constant for all the CFS models are as under:

Uniform effective span of 2.1m.

Identical simple support conditions.

Identical two point loading arrangement.

27

Identical size of bearing plates under concentrated loading points.

Identical stiffener arrangement under concentrated loading points.

4.5 Specific Details of Various Test Models

All dimensions are in mm only. The important details along with judiciously proposed specific variations in each Model are described as under:

4.5.1 Group-I   Models Characterised by Simple Fabrication

4.5.1.1 Model A: Unstiffened Model

The sectional geometry of this model consists of I shape using two lipped channel sections back to back as shown in Figure 7. Steel sheet of thickness 2mm has only been used for fabrication of this model. Dimensions of various elements of model are shown in the sectional view of Figure 7(a) .

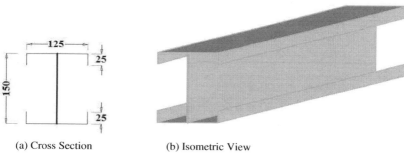

(a) Cross Section   (b) Isometric View

Figure 7: Model A

4.5.1.2 Model B: Angle Stiffened Model

After noticing localized lip buckling mode of failure on compression side within high B M zone at a low value of loading during testing of Model A, it was felt that effective stiffening of compression zone falling under higher BM would have arrested such localized buckling, thus greatly improved its structural performance. Accordingly, Model B, which is a modified version of Model A using two hot rolled angle stiffeners $(25 \times 25 \times 4)$ as shown in the Figure-8 was fabricated to have stiffened compression flange over a length of 1.5m falling under higher bending moment. Rest of the details of Model B are kept strictly identical with Model A so as to investigate experimentally the contribution of the proposed variation in Model B, (that is effective stiffening of compression zone falling under higher B M) towards improved structural performance.

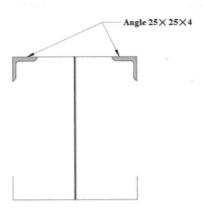

Angle 25×25×4

Figure 8: Cross Section of Model B

4.5.2 Group-II Models Characterised by Box Profiling of Vulnerable Elements

4.5.2.1 Model C: Hollow Box Model

The sectional geometry of this model is also I shaped and consists of hollow rectangular box profile for both vulnerable zones that is compression flange and web, as shown in Figure 9. Only 1.6mm thick sheet has been used for fabrication of this model. Dimensions of various elements of model are shown in the sectional view of Figure 9(a).

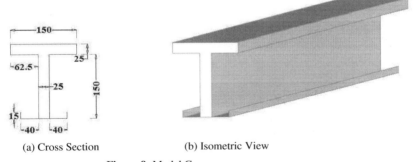

(a) Cross Section   (b) Isometric View

Figure 9: Model C

4.5.2.2 Model D: Box Model Stiffened with Thermocol Packing

Model D is modified version of Model C using specially ordered high density thermocol ($24kg/m^3$) packing as shown in Figure 10 to investigate experimentally its contribution towards stiffening of vulnerable elements, particularly, compression flange against buckling as well as punching or bearing modes of failure under point loads. Only 1.6mm thick sheet has been used for fabrication of this model. Dimensions of various elements of model are shown in the sectional view of Figure 10 (a).

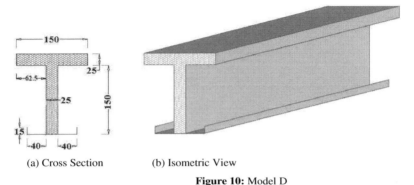

(a) Cross Section   (b) Isometric View

Figure 10: Model D

4.5.2.3 Model E: Box Model packed mainly with Thermocol& locally with wooden pads under concentrated loads

After noticing localized punching mode of failure on compression side under concentrated loads during testing of Models C and D, it was felt that stiffer packing material like wood might have arrested such localized failure, thus greatly improving its structural performance. Accordingly, Model E, which is a modified version of Model D was fabricated replacing thermocol packing by wooden packing at the location of the concentrated loading points as shown in the Figure 11. Rest of the details of Model E are kept strictly identical with Model D so as to investigate experimentally the contribution of the proposed variation in Model E, (that is stiffer packing material like wood under point loads) to avoid localized punching failure at these locations.

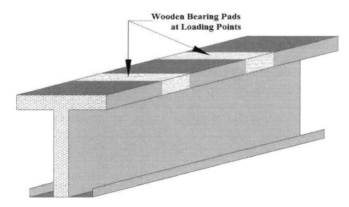

Figure 11: Isometric View of Model E

4.5.3 Group-III Models Characterised by Simple Fabrication &Timber Stiffening of Vulnerable Elements

4.5.3.1 Model F: Timber stiffened Model without Lip.

Having noticed the great advantages of simple fabrication in *GROUP I* models as well as promising contribution by wooden packing in *Model E*, it was concluded to combine the above favorable features in next series of models for achieving much improved structural performance. Accordingly, Model F with unsymmetrical I shape (using two lipped channel sections back to back like Model A) involving simple fabrication was fabricated. The vulnerable elements, namely compression zone and web were stiffened by firmly attaching timber planks as shown in Figure 12. Sufficient number of bolts were used to achieve the desired composite action. Only 1.6mm thick sheet has been used for fabrication of this model. Dimensions of various elements of model are shown in Figure 12 (a).

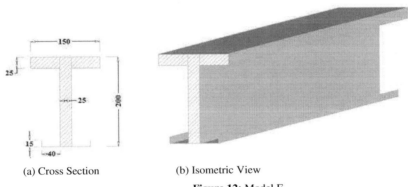

(a) Cross Section   (b) Isometric View

Figure 12: Model F

4.5.3.2 Model G: Timber Stiffened Model with Lip Strengthening

Having noticed localized lip failure of Model F in high B M zone, it was felt to improve its performance by strengthening lips against such failure. Accordingly, Model G which is a modified version of Model F was fabricated by strengthening the lips using steel strips as shown in Figure 13 at intervals within the central zone of 1.5m falling under higher B M.

31

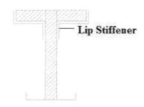

Figure 13: Cross Section of Model G

4.5.3.3 Model H: Light Weight Timber Stiffened Model

Having noticed promising contribution by timber stiffening in Models F and G, it was felt to investigate such stiffening arrangement for much lighter CFS models. Accordingly, an attempt was made to fabricate model H which consists of symmetrical I shape using two lipped channel sections back to back and stiffened with timber planks as shown in Figure 14. Sufficient bolts were used to achieve the desired composite action. Only1.2mm thick sheet has been used for fabrication of this model. Dimensions of various elements of model are shown in Figure 14(a).

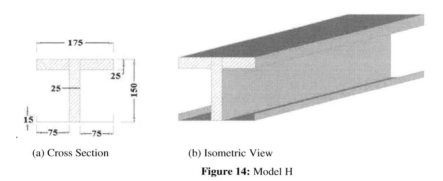

(a) Cross Section   (b) Isometric View

Figure 14: Model H

4.5.4 Group-IV Models Characterized by Simple Fabrication &Lightest in Weight

4.5.4.1 Model I: Unstiffened Lightest Model

Having noticed the great advantages of simple fabrication in GROUP I models as well as the importance of achieving steel economy, it was felt necessary to fabricate lighter models using thinnest possible steel sheets. Accordingly, Model I with symmetrical I shape (using two lipped channel sections back to back like Model A) involving simple fabrication was fabricated as shown in Figure 15. Only 1 mm thick sheet has been used for fabrication of this model. Dimensions of various elements of model are shown in Figure 15 (a).

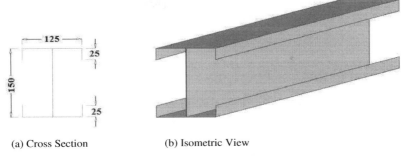

(a) Cross Section   (b) Isometric View

Figure 15: Model I

4.5.4.2 Model J: Stiffened Lightest Model

Having noticed localized lip failure of Model I in high B M zone, it was felt to improve its performance by strengthening lips against such failure. Accordingly, Model J which is a modified version of Model I was fabricated by strengthening the lips using steel strips as shown in Figure 16 at intervals within the central zone of 1.5m falling under higher B. M.

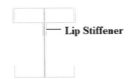

Figure 16: Cross Section of Model J

4.5.5 Group-V Model of Hot Rolled Section (Reference Model for comparison)

By developing structurally efficient CFS beam sections steel economy was taken into consideration. But it was necessary to evaluate them from structural response consideration too. Therefore Model K i.e,ISMB-150 was chosen as reference model for meaningful comparison between the above Model and various CFS beam sections with innovative solutions. Figure 17 shows the isometric view of Model K.

Figure 17: Isometric View of Model K

4.6 Role of Bearing Stiffeners

Bearing stiffeners are required at the point of application of concentrated loads and reaction. It prevents the web from crushing and sideways buckling under the concentrated load. Load bearing stiffeners must be provided at all points carrying concentrated load or reaction as shown in Figure 18. A bearing stiffener consists one or more pair of angles connected on both sides of the web. The bearing stiffeners at the support points should project as nearly as possible to the outer edges of the flanges. Bearing stiffeners are also meant to provide restraint against torsion at the ends. (Arya A.S. & Ajmani J.L., 2012)

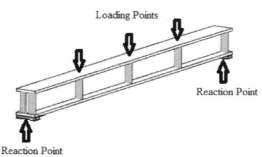

Figure 18: Bearing Stiffeners under Reaction &Concentrated Loading Points

4.7 Material Testing

Various standards exist which specify the requirements for the testing of tensile specimens. Three tensile test specimens were prepared from 2 mm steel sheet in accordance with IS 1608-2005 as shown in Figure 19. This allowed the determination of an accurate stress-strain relationship for steel. The material properties of CFS have shown to be anisotropic (Wu S. et al., 1995, Dhalla and Winter, 1971).

34

Hence all the tensile test specimens were cut in the longitudinal direction with respect to the rolling direction of steel sheets, as it was the same longitudinal direction along which the test beams used for section and member capacities were made. Specimen size and shape are important variables which can affect its behavior. Accurate and consistent fabrication procedures were used for all specimens included in this test program to ensure that test specimens were of near identical size and shape. All the tensile tests were conducted on precision universal testing machine as shown in the Figure 20. To record the deformation dial gauge was mounted and the deformation was noted as every 0.4KN. The typical stress strain curve of tensile test is as shown in the Figure 21 all three tensile test coupons showed an approximate yield stress of about 260.3N/mm^2.The pattern of yielding of the test coupons can be seen in Figure 22.

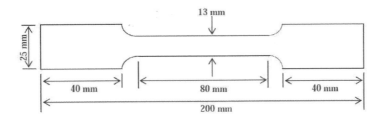

Figure 19: Nominal Size of the Tensile Test Specimen

Figure 20: Tensile Test Specimen in the U.T.M.

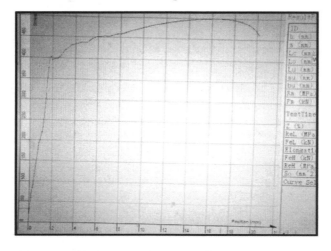

Figure21: Typical Load Displacement Curve of Tensile Test

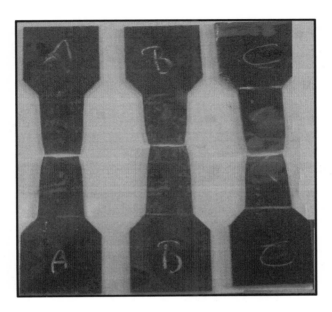

Figure 22: Test Specimens after Tensile Test

4.8 Theoretical Design and Analysis of Selected Models

Before carrying out experimental testing of various models, it is logical to carryout detailed analytical design and analysis of these models based on stipulated procedures well documented in national and international codes. Accordingly this section presents the detailed theoretical design and analysis for selected models only to avoid. Similar theoretical design and analysis for other models are presented in Appendix-A

4.8.1.1 Design & Analysis of Loading of Group I Models (Model A/ Model B) According to IS-801

Basic design stress f=0.6f$_y$=0.6 ×250=150N/mm² (for stiffened compression elements)

Determination of effective design width

$$b = \left(\frac{125}{2}\right) = 62.5 \text{ and, } t = 2$$

Then, $\quad b/_t = \left(\frac{62.5}{2}\right) = 31.25$

But according to Clause 5.2.1.1 of IS 801-1975

$$\left(b/_t\right)_{lim} = \left(\frac{446}{\sqrt{f}}\right)$$

$$= \left(\frac{446}{\sqrt{150}}\right)$$

$$= 36.4 \text{ N/mm}^2$$

As seen above,

$$\left(b/_t\right) < \left(b/_t\right)_{lim}$$

Therefore,

$$b = w = 62.5\text{mm}$$

Where, w = width of the flange; t = thickness of the flange & f_y = yield stress.

Design of edge stiffener

According to Clause 5.2.2 of I.S. 801-1975

The edge stiffener must have minimum moment of inertia equal to

$$I_{min} = 1.83t^4 \sqrt{\left(b/_t\right)^2 - \left(\frac{27590}{f_y}\right)} > 9.2t^4$$

$$I_{min} = 1.83 \times 2^4 \sqrt{(31.25)^2 - \left(\frac{27590}{250}\right)}$$

$$I_{min} = 29.28 \sqrt{[976.56 - 183.9}$$

$$I_{min} = 824.3\text{mm}^4$$

Now,

$$9.2 \times t^4 = 147.2$$

$$I_{min} > 9.2 \times t^4$$

Hence it is ok.

When the stiffener lip consists of a simple lip bent at right angel to stiffened element, the required overall depth d_{min} of such lip is

$$d_{min} = 2.8 \times t \left[\left(\frac{b}{t} \right)^2 - \left(\frac{27590}{f_y} \right) \right]^{\frac{1}{6}}$$

$$= 2.8 \times 2 \left[(31.25)^2 - 110.36 \right]^{\frac{1}{6}}$$

$$= 17.28 \approx 20mm$$

$$d_{min} = 20mm$$

Determination of Sectional properties.

$$I_{xx} = 4 \left[\left(\frac{2 \times 25^3}{12} \right) + 2 \times 25 \times 62.5^2 \right] + 2[2 \times 125 \times 75^2] + \left[\frac{4 \times 150^3}{12} \right]$$

$$I_{xx} = [7.9 \times 10^5 + 28 \times 10^5 + 11.25 \times 10^5]$$

$$I_{xx} = 47.25 \times 10^5 mm^4$$

Now,

$$Z = \left(\frac{I_{xx}}{\overline{Y}} \right)$$

$$Z = \left(\frac{47.25 \times 10^5}{75} \right)$$

$$Z = 63000 \ mm^3$$

Determination of Moment &Load carrying Capacity

$$M = fZ$$

$$M = 150 \times 63000$$

$$M = 9.45kNm$$

Where I_{xx} is the moment of inertia of section horizontal axis passing through centroid of the section.

$\overline{Y}$ is the distance of extreme fiber in compression from neutral axis.

Z is the sectional modulus.

& M is the moment carrying capacity

For a beam under two point loading, the load carrying capacity (W) is

$$W = \left(2 \times \frac{9.45}{0.7} \right)$$

W = 27 kN

Determination of Sectional properties.

The distance of extreme fiber in compression from neutral axis is

$$\overline{Y} = 75mm$$

Moment of Inertia of the Section

$$I_{xx} = 4\left[\left(\frac{2 \times 25^3}{12}\right) + 2 \times 25 \times 62.5^2\right] + 2\left[\left(\frac{125 \times 2^3}{12}\right) + 125 \times 2 \times 75^2\right] + \left[\frac{4 \times 150^3}{12}\right]$$

$$I_{xx} = 8 \times 10^5 + 28 \times 10^5 + 11.25 \times 10^5$$
$$I_{xx} = 47.25 \times 10^5 \text{ mm}^4$$

$$\Sigma I_{xx} = 47.25 \times 10^5 \text{mm}^4$$

Now Sectional Modulus,

$$Z_y = \left(\frac{\Sigma I_{xx}}{\overline{Y}}\right)$$

$$Z_y = \left(\frac{47.25 \times 10^5}{75}\right)$$

$$Z_y = 63000 \text{ mm}^3$$

$$M_y = Z_y \times f_y$$

$$M_y = 9.45 \text{ KNm.}$$

Determination of effective design width

1. $$\lambda = \frac{1.05}{\sqrt{4}}\left(\frac{125}{2}\sqrt{\frac{250}{2 \times 10^5}}\right)$$
       $$\lambda = 1.162$$
       This shows that $\lambda > 0.673$
∴ $$b_e = \rho b$$

       $$\rho = \left(\frac{1 - \frac{0.22}{1.162}}{1.162}\right)$$

       $$\rho = 0.69$$

∴ $$b_e = 0.69 \times 125$$

40

$b_e = 87.2$ mm

2. $\psi = \left(\frac{166.67}{250}\right)$

$\psi = 0.67$

$k = 4+2(1-0.67)^3+2(1-0.67) = 4.73$

$\lambda = \frac{1.052}{\sqrt{4.73}}\left(\frac{25}{2}\sqrt{\frac{250}{2\times10^5}}\right)$

$\lambda = 0.21$

$\lambda < 0.673$

$b_e = b = 25$mm

3. $\psi = \left(\frac{250}{250}\right) = 1$

$k = 4 + 2(1+1)^3 + 2(1+1)$

$k = 24$

$\lambda = \left(\frac{1.052}{\sqrt{24}}\right)\left(\frac{75}{2}\sqrt{\frac{250}{2\times10^5}}\right)$

$\lambda = 0.28$

$\lambda < 0.673$

$\therefore \quad b_e = b = 150$

$b_{e1} = \left(\frac{b_e}{3+1}\right)$

$b_{e1} = \left(\frac{150}{3+1}\right) = 37.5$

$b_{e2} = \left(\frac{b_e}{2}\right) = 75$

$b_{e1} + b_{e2} = 37.5 + 75 = 112.5 > \left(\frac{b}{2}\right)$

$\therefore \quad b_e = 75$mm

Determination of Modified Sectional Properties

Element	b_e	t	A	$\bar{Y}$	$A\bar{Y}$
1	87.2	2	174.4	0	0

2	25	2	50	12.5	625
3C	75	2	150	37.5	5625
3T	75	2	150	112.5	16875
4	87.2	2	174.4	150	26160
5	25	2	50	137.5	6875
			$\Sigma A = 748.8$		$\Sigma A\overline{Y} = 56160$

Table 1: Modified Sectional Properties of Group-I Models

Distance to neutral axis from top is

$$Y'=\left(\frac{\Sigma A\overline{Y}}{\Sigma A}\right)=\frac{56160}{748.8}$$

$Y'=75mm$

Now, $\quad Z_e = \left(\frac{\Sigma I_{xx}}{Y'}\right)$

$$Z_e= \left(\frac{47.25 \times 10^5}{75}\right)$$

$Z_e=63000mm^3$

Determination of Moment & Load Carrying Capacity

$M_s=Z_e\times f_Y$

$M_s=63000\times 250$

$M_s=9.45kN\text{-}m$

$W =\left(\frac{9.45}{0.7}\times 2\right) = 27kN \qquad \boxed{W =27kN}$

4.9 Fabrication of Models

To fabricate the required beam modes the steel sheets where cut to required width using Sheet Shearing Machine as shown in Figure 23.Once the sheet was cut to required dimension marking was done on the sheet as to where the sheet had to be pressed to get the required sectional profile, after the marking was done the sheet was pressed using Hydraulic Pressing Machine as shown in the Figure 24. Once the required sectional profiles were obtained, it was necessary to assemble them as per the requirement by means of bolted connections with necessary drilling as shown in Figure 25.

Figure 23: Sheet Shearing Machine **Figure**   **24:** Hydraulic Pressing Machine

Figure 25: Drilling Operation for Bolted Connection

Chapter-5
Experimental Testing & Data Recording

5.1 Necessity of Experimental Testing

For successful achievement of structural engineering objectives, it is of prime importance to have sound understanding of structural response of a structure under different loading conditions. Although there are number of analytical methods/computer software packages for obtaining the desired structural response, however, under certain practical situations like complex structural configurations, intricate connection/support conditions, these sophisticated structures may not be amenable to the existing analytical/computer methods hence cannot be analyzed with accuracy desired. In spite of great engineering and technological advancement in structural engineering profession, there are numerous well identified challenging problems for which innovative solutions need to be developed for providing efficient professional services to the society. It needs to be highlighted here that experimental techniques have a great potential for exploring the original creative ideas, thus leading to the development of desired innovative solutions for challenging problems.

Because of its overwhelming advantages, the use of CFS members has rapidly increased in recent years. However, their structural behavior characterized by various buckling modes is not yet fully understood thus making it one of the challenging research areas in structural engineering. Flexural members being prime members in most of the structures, hence there is an urgent need in the CFS industry to explore new innovative CFS beam sections for improved structural performance. Accordingly, an attempt has been made in the present work to explore experimentally the potential innovative solutions for much improved structural performance of CFS beam sections. Details of extensive experimental testing and data recording are presented in this chapter.

5.2 Testing Programme & Necessary Precautions

Experimental testing of all the beam models were performed using 500kN capacity Beam Testing Rig described in chapter 4. For obtaining the reliable and good quality experimental data, it is very important to take necessary precautions and ensuring high precision at all stages of testing programme. The important stages of testing programme are described as under:

5.2.1 Mounting of Test Specimen & Supporting Arrangement

The test specimen as well as the supporting frame was positioned symmetrically with reference to centre point of loading rig to ensure symmetric two point loading arrangement for each test. All the necessary adjustments (including insertion of thin packing at supports if required for leveling) were accomplished to ensure that centre line of steel bearing plates (firmly attached with bottom flange at support locations) and centre line of rounded simple support are aligned.

5.2.2 Loading System

The simply supported beam specimens were tested by loading them symmetrically at two points on the span through a spreader rigid beam which was loaded centrally by the ram of the 500kN capacity hydraulic loading jack. All the tests were conducted with symmetric loading points at a distance of one third of the span from the supports. Such a loading arrangement provided uniform maximum BM and zero SF within central one third of span. To prevent the localized pre mature bearing failure at applied loading points, suitable size bearing pads were used for smooth transfer of concentrated loads from spreader beam to test beam through roller/steel pad at each loading point.

5.2.3 Data Measuring System

High precision data measuring systems used in all the tests are described as under:

1) Load Measurement System

The load applied centrally over the rigid spreader beam was measured using 100kN capacity high precision proving ring shown in Figure 26

Figure 26: High Precision Proving Ring

2) *Deflection Measurement System*

High precision Dial gauges with 50mm travel and 25mm travel were mounted at three vital locations as shown in Figure 27 to measure deflections during testing. Deflections at all the three locations were recorded at suitable load increment. All the models were tested up to their failure level attained in each case.

Figure 27: High Precision Dial Gauges

5.2.4   Necessary Precautions

For each test, following precautions were taken before the start of testing to rule out any error in the recorded data:

Check for Verticality of loading jack and its positioning to ensure in-plane loading.

Check for Verticality of dial gauges.

Check for Symmetric load application.

Check for Symmetric support locations.

5.3 Detailed Testing of various beam models

The sequence of testing conducted on various beam models and recording of relevant data during each test are described as under:

Model A: Unstiffened Model with Simple Fabrication

Model A was mounted on the Testing Rig as shown in the Figure 28 and the data recorded is given in Table 2.

Figure 28: Model A mounted on the Testing Rig

Sr. No.	Load (kN)	Deflection (mm)		Sr. No.	Load (kN)	Deflection (mm)	
		Mid span	2/3rd span			Mid span	2/3rd span
1	0	0	0	8	23.1875	5.87	5.60
2	3.3125	0.18	0.17	9	26.5000	6.75	6.43
3	6.6250	1.15	1.11	10	29.8125	7.71	7.32
4	9.9375	2.18	2.08	11	33.1250	8.61	8.18
5	13.2500	3.17	3.00	12	36.4375	9.62	9.10
6	16.5625	4.04	3.84	13	39.7500	10.59	10.00
7	19.8750	5.00	4.78	14	43.0625	11.67	11.01

Table 2: Load Displacement Values for Model A

Model B: Angle stiffened Model with simple fabrication

Model B was mounted on the Testing Rig as shown in the Figure 29 and the data recorded is given in Table 3

Figure 29: Model B mounted on the Testing Rig

Sr. No.	Load (kN)	Deflection (mm)		Sr. No.	Load (kN)	Deflection (mm)	
		Mid span	2/3rd span			Mid span	2/3rd span
1	0	0	0	14	58.300	10.20	10.06
2	10.600	1.85	1.64	15	59.625	10.53	10.35
3	21.200	3.59	3.18	16	60.950	10.95	10.74
4	31.800	5.41	4.8	17	62.275	11.55	11.28
5	42.400	7.28	6.45	18	63.600	12.14	11.76
6	45.050	7.72	6.84	19	64.925	12.82	12.36
7	47.700	8.19	7.25	20	66.250	13.42	12.86
8	50.350	8.61	7.64	21	67.575	14.92	14.13
9	51.675	8.90	7.89	22	67.840	15.82	14.89
10	53.000	9.18	8.13	23	68.105	16.68	15.63
11	54.325	9.34	8.29	24	67.840	18.58	17.23
12	55.650	9.64	8.55	25	67.840	20.70	18.97
13	56.975	9.95	8.84	26	67.840	21.70	19.70

Table 3: Load Displacement Values for Model B

Model C: Hollow Box Model

Model C was mounted on the Testing Rig as shown in the Figure 30 and the data recorded is given in Table 4

Figure 30: Model C mounted on the Testing Rig

Sr. No.	Load (kN)	Deflection (mm) 2/3rd span	Deflection (mm) Mid span	Sr. No.	Load (kN)	Deflection (mm) 2/3rd span	Deflection (mm) Mid span
1	0	0	0	21	16.38	7.58	9.80
2	0.78	2.30	4.33	22	16.90	7.75	9.98
3	1.56	2.54	4.58	23	17.94	8.24	10.45
4	2.34	2.80	4.86	24	19.24	8.76	11.01
5	3.12	3.12	5.17	25	20.02	8.95	11.21
6	3.90	3.34	5.37	26	20.54	9.20	11.48
7	4.68	3.70	5.77	27	20.80	9.34	11.61
8	5.46	3.99	6.01	28	21.32	9.55	11.84
9	6.24	4.24	6.31	29	21.58	9.68	11.99
10	7.02	4.55	6.65	30	22.62	10.08	12.55
11	7.80	4.80	6.93	31	23.40	10.41	12.89
12	8.50	5.08	7.21	32	23.92	10.68	13.18
13	9.62	5.40	7.55	33	24.44	10.92	13.44
14	10.4	5.58	7.72	34	24.96	11.23	13.74
15	11.8	5.88	8.02	35	25.22	11.46	14.18
16	12.22	6.30	8.43	36	26.00	11.98	14.48
17	13.00	6.45	8.62	37	26.26	12.23	14.75
18	14.04	6.75	8.91	38	27.04	12.56	15.05

19	14.82	7.02	9.20		39	27.30	12.88	15.38
20	15.60	7.34	9.50					

Table 4: Load Displacement Values for Model C

Model D: Box Model Stiffened with Thermocol packing

Model D was mounted on the Testing Rig as shown in the Figure 31 and the data recorded is given in Table 5

Figure 31: Model D mounted on the Testing Rig

Sr. No.	Load (kN)	Deflection (mm) 2/3rd span	Deflection (mm) Mid span	Sr. No.	Load (kN)	Deflection (mm) 2/3rd span	Deflection (mm) Mid span
1	0	0	0	9	15.00	2.61	2.10
2	1.88	0.22	0.15	10	16.88	2.99	2.40
3	3.88	0.54	0.42	11	18.75	3.36	2.70
4	5.63	0.87	0.68	12	20.63	3.74	3.00
5	7.50	1.20	0.95	13	22.50	4.14	3.31
6	9.38	1.56	1.25	14	24.38	4.53	3.62
7	11.25	1.92	1.54	15	25.63	4.96	3.95
8	13.13	2.26	1.80				

Table 5: Load Displacement Values for Model D

Model E: Box Model packed with Thermocol all through but wooden packing locally under concentrated load points

Model E was mounted on the Testing Rig as shown in the Figure 32 and the data recorded is given in Table 6

Figure 32: Model E mounted on the Testing Rig

Sr. No.	Load (kN)	Deflection (mm)		Sr. No.	Load (kN)	Deflection (mm)	
		Mid span	2/3rd span			Mid span	2/3rd span
1	0	0	0	15	26.25	5.79	4.70
2	1.88	0.36	0.28	16	28.13	6.26	5.10
3	3.75	0.75	0.59	17	30.00	6.78	5.55
4	5.63	1.12	0.90	18	31.88	7.36	6.01
5	7.50	1.51	1.20	19	33.75	7.91	6.46
6	9.38	1.93	1.55	20	35.00	8.39	6.86
7	11.25	2.35	1.90	21	36.25	8.82	7.21
8	13.13	2.79	2.26	22	37.50	9.45	7.71
9	15.00	3.15	2.58	23	38.75	10.15	8.25
10	16.88	3.60	2.94	24	40.00	11.00	8.94
11	18.75	4.03	3.28	25	41.25	12.45	10.01
12	20.63	4.46	3.62	26	41.88	13.50	11.85
13	22.50	4.89	3.97	27	42.50	14.64	12.80
14	24.38	5.31	4.31				

Table 6: Load Displacement Values for Model E

Model F: Timber stiffened Model without Lip strengthening (Simple Fabrication)

Model F was mounted on the Testing Rig as shown in the Figure 33 and the data recorded is given in Table 7

Figure 33: Model F mounted on the Testing Rig

Sr. No.	Load (kN)	Deflection (mm)		Sr. No.	Load (kN)	Deflection (mm)	
		Mid span	2/3rd span			Mid span	2/3rd span
1	0	0	0	21	37.500	7.90	7.45
2	1.875	0.39	0.34	22	39.375	8.33	7.85
3	3.750	0.70	0.63	23	41.250	8.65	8.14
4	5.625	1.05	0.98	24	43.125	8.98	8.42
5	7.500	1.42	1.34	25	45.000	9.41	8.81
6	9.375	1.89	1.81	26	46.875	9.73	9.10
7	11.250	2.29	2.22	27	48.750	10.25	9.55
8	13.125	2.76	2.72	28	50.625	10.54	9.83
9	15.000	3.15	3.10	29	52.500	10.90	10.07
10	16.875	3.55	3.51	30	54.375	11.29	10.53
11	18.750	3.92	3.87	31	56.250	11.66	10.87
12	20.625	4.33	4.27	32	58.125	12.15	11.30
13	22.500	4.70	4.63	33	60.000	12.43	11.57
14	24.375	5.10	5.00	34	61.875	13.14	12.21
15	26.250	5.42	5.29	35	63.750	13.70	12.71
16	28.125	5.82	5.65	36	65.000	14.12	13.08
17	30.000	6.17	5.97	37	66.250	14.54	13.46
18	31.875	6.65	6.36	38	67.500	14.99	13.86
19	33.750	7.03	6.69	39	68.750	15.40	14.24
20	35.625	7.46	7.07	40	70.000	16.08	14.85

Table 7: Load Displacement Values for Model F

Model G: Timber stiffened model with Lip strengthening (Simple Fabrication)

Model G was mounted on the Testing Rig as shown in the Figure 34 and the data recorded is given in Table 8

Figure 34: Model G mounted on the Testing Rig

53

Sr. No.	Load (kN)	Deflection (mm) Mid span	Deflection (mm) 2/3rd span	Sr. No.	Load (kN)	Deflection (mm) Mid span	Deflection (mm) 2/3rd span
1	0	0	0	23	41.250	7.05	6.42
2	1.875	0.39	0.30	24	43.125	7.35	6.69
3	3.750	0.89	0.70	25	45.000	7.61	6.94
4	5.625	1.33	1.07	26	46.875	7.89	7.20
5	7.500	1.65	1.36	27	48.750	8.15	7.44
6	9.375	2.04	1.72	28	50.625	8.43	7.69
7	11.250	2.47	2.11	29	52.500	8.70	7.93
8	13.125	2.80	2.42	30	54.375	9.00	8.21
9	15.000	3.13	2.73	31	56.250	9.34	8.51
10	16.875	3.43	3.02	32	58.125	9.60	8.75
11	18.750	3.72	3.30	33	60.000	9.90	9.03
12	20.625	4.01	3.57	34	61.875	10.25	9.35
13	22.500	4.33	3.86	35	63.750	10.65	9.71
14	24.375	4.59	4.12	36	65.000	11.22	10.21
15	26.250	4.89	4.40	37	66.250	11.49	10.45
16	28.125	5.14	4.62	38	67.500	11.85	10.79
17	30.000	5.39	4.86	39	68.750	12.28	11.24
18	31.875	5.70	5.16	40	70.625	13.65	12.44
19	33.750	5.94	5.39	41	71.875	14.50	13.50
20	35.625	6.24	5.66	42	73.125	15.85	14.75
21	37.500	6.50	5.90	43	74.375	17.70	16.90
22	39.375	6.77	6.16				

Table 8: Load Displacement Values for Model G

Model H: Light weight Timber stiffened model (Simple Fabrication)

Model H was mounted on the Testing Rig as shown in the Figure 35 and the data recorded is given in Table 9

Figure 35: Model H mounted on the Testing Rig

Sr. No.	Load (kN)	Deflection (mm) Mid span	2/3rd span	Sr. No.	Load (kN)	Deflection (mm) Mid span	2/3rd span
1	0	0	0	18	21.250	9.93	8.25
2	1.250	0.52	0.46	19	22.500	10.10	8.95
3	2.500	0.99	0.88	20	23.125	10.65	9.43
4	3.750	1.51	1.36	21	23.750	11.20	9.91
5	5.000	1.98	1.77	22	24.375	11.70	10.35
6	6.250	2.50	2.23	23	25.000	12.30	10.74
7	7.500	3.06	2.72	24	25.625	12.64	11.17
8	8.750	3.63	3.22	25	26.250	13.48	11.91
9	10.000	4.25	3.76	26	26.875	13.89	12.28
10	11.250	4.75	4.20	27	27.500	14.74	13.04
11	12.500	5.30	4.67	28	28.125	16.90	14.46
12	13.750	5.82	5.13	29	28.750	17.85	14.93
13	15.000	6.35	5.60	30	29.375	19.60	15.78
14	16.250	6.92	6.09	31	30.000	20.60	17.30
15	17.500	7.47	6.6	32	30.625	22.40	18.17
16	18.750	8.03	7.09	33	31.250	25.90	19.72
17	20.000	8.63	7.62				

Table 9: Load Displacement Values for Model H

Model I: Unstiffened Lightest Model (Simple Fabrication)

Model I was mounted on the Testing Rig as shown in the Figure 36 and the data recorded is given in Table 10

Figure 36: Model I mounted on the Testing Rig

Sr. No.	Load (kN)	Deflection (mm)		Sr. No.	Load (kN)	Deflection (mm)	
		Mid span	2/3rd span			Mid span	2/3rd span
1	0	0	0	12	6.875	2.20	2.13
2	0.625	0.20	0.22	13	7.500	2.44	2.35
3	1.250	0.39	0.40	14	8.125	2.64	2.55
4	1.875	0.58	0.59	15	8.750	2.89	2.80
5	2.500	0.75	0.75	16	9.375	3.15	3.05
6	3.125	0.96	0.95	17	10.00	3.37	3.26
7	3.750	1.17	1.14	18	10.625	3.63	3.53
8	4.375	1.41	1.37	19	11.250	3.88	3.78
9	5.000	1.58	1.54	20	11.875	4.18	4.10
10	5.625	1.77	1.72	21	12.500	4.48	4.41
11	6.250	1.99	1.93	22	13.125	5.04	5.01

Table 10: Load Displacement Values for Model I

Model J: *Stiffened Lightest Model (Simple Fabrication)*

Model J was mounted on the Testing Rig as shown in the Figure 37 and the data recorded is given in Table 11.

Figure 37: Model J mounted on the Testing Rig

Sr. No.	Load (kN)	Deflection (mm) Mid span	Deflection (mm) 2/3rd span	Sr. No.	Load (kN)	Deflection (mm) Mid span	Deflection (mm) 2/3rd span
1	0	0	0	9	10.00	3.30	2.65
2	1.25	0.26	0.17	10	11.25	3.63	3.08
3	2.50	0.64	0.50	11	12.50	4.30	3.67
4	3.75	1.01	0.83	12	13.125	4.55	3.85
5	5.00	1.44	1.19	13	13.750	4.87	4.12
6	6.25	1.86	1.56	14	14.375	5.24	4.45
7	7.50	2.29	1.92	15	15.000	6.16	5.05
8	8.75	2.75	2.31				

Table 11: Load Displacement Values for Model J

5.3.5 Testing of Group V Models
Model K: ISMB-150

Model K was mounted on the Testing Rig as shown in the Figure 38 and and the data recorded is given in Table 12

Figure 38: Model K mounted on the Testing Rig

Sr. No.	Load (kN)	Deflection (mm)		Sr. No.	Load (kN)	Deflection (mm)	
		Mid span	2/3rd span			Mid span	2/3rd span
1	0	0	0	11	41.50	8.63	7.61
2	4.15	1.03	0.90	12	45.65	9.40	8.31
3	8.30	2.08	1.72	13	49.75	10.30	8.84
4	12.45	2.95	2.48	14	58.90	11.51	10.05
5	16.60	3.86	3.28	15	63.05	12.07	10.74
6	20.75	4.76	4.10	16	68.20	12.95	11.48
7	24.90	5.50	4.77	17	74.35	13.82	12.23
8	29.05	6.30	5.53	18	79.50	14.65	12.94
9	33.20	7.05	6.20	19	83.65	16.00	14.02
10	37.35	7.87	6.94				

Table 12: Load Displacement Values for Model K

Chapter-6

Data Analysis, Result Interpretation & Discussion

6.1 General

The experimental data recorded during testing of different beam models (categorized in four well defined groups in Chapter-IV) with specific variations needs to be judiciously analyzed to facilitate the meaningful interpretation of the experimental results. This chapter presents the detailed analysis of the data recorded during the testing of each model recognized by well-defined variations in sectional characteristics, stiffening arrangements etc. The analyzed data will be followed by necessary interpretation and discussion highlighting the promising results of experimental investigations.

6.2 Graphical Mode of Data Presentation

Experimental testing of a structure (or its component) provides the best source to get a physical feel about the structural response to applied loading. Graphical representation of experimental data in the form of load v/s vertical deflection curves serves an ideal tool for distinct and meaningful interpretation of experimental results. Accordingly, the transformation of experimental data (recorded for various tests in tabular form in Chapter-V) into graphical form is presented in this chapter to facilitate its purposeful interpretation.

6.3 Test Results, Interpretation and Discussion

According to the standard criteria being adopted for beam section classification (i.e. limits of width to thickness ratios of constituent plate elements of beam section), all the CFS beam test specimens considered in this work were classified as slender, hence most of the specimens were expected to experience premature local buckling before they reach the first yield moment. Such a premature failure takes place at much lower loads than full carrying capacity. The distinct and prominently noticeable changes visible in experimental results contributed by the proposed physical variations introduced in each test model greatly facilitate the desired purposeful interpretation. Accordingly, it was deemed most appropriate to consider presentation of experimental results in following four groups consistent with classification of models already described in Chapter-IV.

It also needs to be highlighted here that experimentally measured load carrying capacity is generally found lower than theoretically predicted capacity and this could be attributed to several factors. The prominent such factors include residual stresses produced due to cold forming and initial geometric imperfections present in the test models. Since all the test models were fabricated manually (see Chapter-IV) and therefore only limited control on the shape and size of specimens could be achieved

59

during the forming/fabrication process. Thus test models had noticeable amount of irregularities in the shape (i.e. geometric imperfections) and in size, which could have contributed towards decrease in the experimentally measured load carrying capacities governed by the amount of irregularities.

6.3.1 Test results and Discussion of Group-I Models

Simple fabrication (which play important role in CFS construction) has been the special characteristics of models under this group. Moreover codal design rules are also available for such simple CFS sections, thus facilitating theoretical prediction about load carrying capacity of such sections with reasonable accuracy. There were two models in this group named as Model A and Model B. This section presents experimental curves of applied load versus in-plane vertical deflection of the models for selected tests only to avoid repetition in interpretation and discussion. Similar experimental curves of other recorded data are presented in Appendix-B.

Figure 39 shows the experimental load v/s displacement curve of Model A at mid span. The curve demonstrates linear response until it experienced premature local buckling failure in the lip within the central one third span with maximum BM. It is worth highlighting here that the said failure was prominently noticed as seen in Figure 40 corresponding to maximum load of 43kN and mid span displacement of 11.67mm. At this stage, the model suddenly stopped resisting any further load, hence rightly called failure load of Model A. Except a localized lip failure confined to very small length, rest of the model was in sound condition and still possessing enough reserve strength.

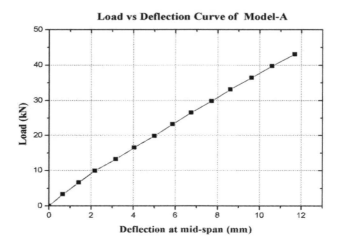

60

Figure 39: Load Displacement Curve at Mid Span for Model A

Figure 40: Lip Buckling of Model A

To exploit this reserved strength it was deemed appropriate to rectify the Model A by strengthening the vulnerable zone within higher bending moment. Accordingly, Angle section 25×25×4 over a central length of 1.5m was welded from inside on both lips to provide required additional stiffening and has been rightly called as angle stiffened model and named as Model B of Group-I.

Figure 41 shows the experimental load deflection curve of the Model B. The curve demonstrates a linear response during initial stage of the loading up to point A. Following the departure from elastic linearity, the beam continued to resist the further application of load confirmed by the rising segment of the curve from point A to point B. The resistance offered by the beam beyond point A up to B was partly due to reserve capacity of the section and partly due to strain hardening. Beyond point B, the model stopped to offer further resistance but deflection continued up to point C. The curve is flat from point B to C reflecting pure plastic type behavior before failure. The mode of failure initiated with a local buckling of compression flange shown in Figure 42 falling within central 1/3rd and was under highest compressive stress corresponding to a failure load of 67.8kN and maximum deflection 21.7mm at mid span. It is worth highlighting here that the Strengthening measure adopted over a full length of vulnerable zone has greatly contributed to much improved load carrying capacity from 43kN to 67.8kN (i.e. increase by 40%) as is clear from combined plot of two models in Figure 43. This encouraging experimental result confirms the important role of judiciously provided stiffening arrangements in CFS construction.

Load vs Deflection Curve of Model-B

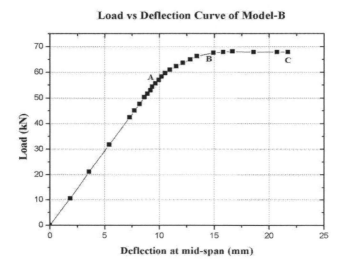

Figure 41: Load Displacement Curve at Mid Span for Model B

Figure 42: Compression flange buckling of Model B

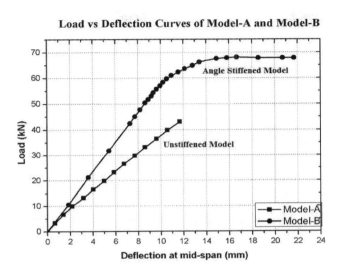

Figure 43: Load Displacement Curves at Mid Span for Model A & B

6.3.2   Test Results & Discussion of Group-II Models

Box profiling followed by stiffening through thermocol packing of vulnerable zones of section i.e. compression flange and web elements has been the special feature of test models under this group. There are no codal design rules available for such CFS sections involving complicated fabrication thus not facilitating theoretical prediction about load carrying capacity of such sections with reasonable accuracy. There were three models in this group named as Models C, D and E. This section presents experimental curves of applied load versus in-plane vertical deflection of these models for selected tests only followed by their interpretation. Similar experimental curves of other recorded data are presented in Appendix-B.

Figure 44 shows the experimental load v/s mid span displacement curve of Model C with hollow box compression flange. The curve exhibits linear response up-to Point A at which it experienced premature local buckling failure in the box compression flange under bearing pads at applied concentrated loading points (apparently seeming like punching failure). From A to B the response was purely plastic. The said failure was noticed as seen in Figure 45 corresponding to failure load of

63

27.3kN and mid span displacement of 12.88mm. The main reason for such a failure was due to non-continuity of bearing stiffeners welded over the web on both sides which carried only up-to lower side of the compression box type element thus leaving the upper side unstiffened at applied loading points. Except a localized buckling failure on top face of box compression flange confined to very small length, rest of the model was found in sound condition and still possessing enough reserve strength.

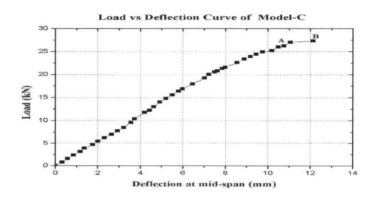

Figure 44: Load Displacement Curve at Mid Span for Model C

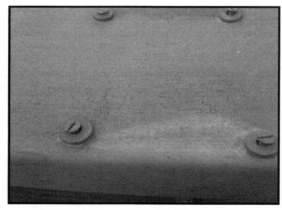

Figure 45: Compression Flange Buckling of Model C (Seems Like punching Failure)

To utilize this reserved strength of Model C, it was well chosen to take necessary remedial measures on Model C. Accordingly, specially ordered high density) thermocol ($24kg/m^3$) was used as continuous packing in vulnerable zones to explore experimentally its contribution towards stiffening of vulnerable elements, particularly, compression flange against buckling as well as punching or bearing modes of failure under point loads and has been rightly called as box model stiffened with themocol packing and was named as Model D.

Figure 46 shows the experimental load v/s mid span displacement curve of Model D. The curve shows a linear response till it experienced similar premature failure, that is, local buckling failure in the box compression flange under bearing pads at applied concentrated loading points. The above failure in this model was accompanied by localized web buckling as well as localized lip buckling under/adjacent to the applied loading points. The said failure modes were noticed as seen in Figure 47 (a), (b) corresponding to failure load of 25.6kN and mid span displacement of 4.96mm. In spite of its high density quality (specially ordered for the purpose), the thermocol packing to act as effective stiffening arrangement (against premature buckling modes of failure) has failed miserably hence was not adopted in further test models.

Except localized buckling failure especially on top face of box compression flange, in both models C and D, restricted to very small length, rest of the Test Model was found in sound condition and still possessing enough reserve strength. After noticing mainly localized punching mode of failure on compression side under concentrated loads during testing of models C and D, it was felt that stiffer packing material like wood might have arrested such localized buckling failure and thus greatly improving its structural performance. Accordingly, Model D, was further rectified by replacing thermocol packing by wooden pads locally under the locations of the concentrated loading points and has been rightly called Box model mainly packed with thermocol but under concentrated load points locally packed with wooden pads. The modified model has been named as Model E.

Rest of the details of Model E were kept strictly identical with Model C and D so as to investigate experimentally the contribution of the proposed improvement in model E, (that is stiffer packing material like wooden pads under point loads) to avoid localized punching like failure at these locations

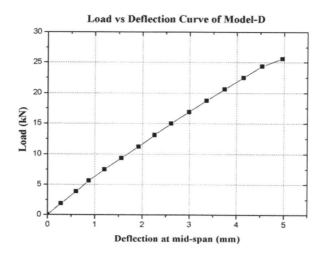

Figure 46: Load Displacement Curve at Mid Span for Model D

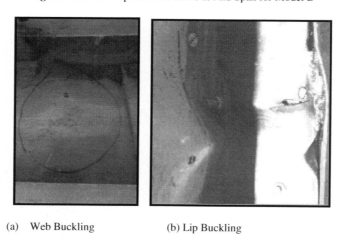

(a)   Web Buckling   (b) Lip Buckling

Figure 47: Failure Modes of Model D

Figure 48 shows the experimental load v/s displacement curve of Model E at mid span. The curve demonstrates a linear response during initial stage of the loading up to point A. Even after the departure from elastic linearity, the beam continued to resist the further application of load confirmed by the rising segment of the curve from point A to point B. The model experienced multiple buckling failure modes particularly, localized web buckling under concentrated applied loads, followed by web buckling away from bolt line near applied load point and finally noticed through lip buckling within high B M zone as seen Figure 49. The resistance offered by the beam beyond point A up to B was partly due to reserve capacity of the section and partly due to strain hardening. It is worth highlighting here that the last mode of failure prominently noticed corresponded to maximum load of 42.5kN and mid span displacement of 14.64mm. It is worth highlighting here that the stiffening measure adopted through local replacement of thermocol by wooden pads at vulnerable spots (i.e. under concentrated applied load points) as shown in Figure 49 (a) has greatly contributed to much improved load carrying capacity from 25.6kN to 42.5kN (i.e. increase by 66%) as is clear from combined plot of three models in Figure 50. Further, the localized failure got transformed into overall failure spread over larger length within high compressive stress. This encouraging experimental result confirms the important role of judiciously provided stiffening arrangements in CFS construction.

The localized web buckling under the point load as shown in Figure 49(b) was observed mainly due to inadequate width of bearing stiffener which could have been arrested by provision of the desired stiffener with adequate width.

Buckling of web away from the bolt as shown in Figure 49(c) was also noticed. This could have been arrested had there been welded connection along the toe of the stiffening angle.

Thermocol packing although with favourable features has failed to produce expected results

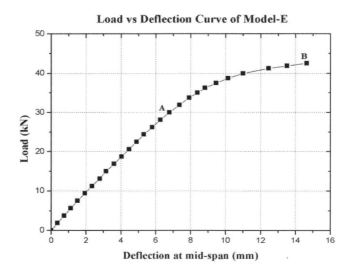

Load vs Deflection Curve of Model-E

Figure 48: Load Displacement Curve at Mid Span for Model B

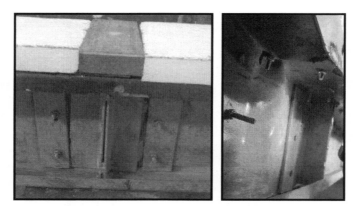

(a) Wooden Bearing under Loading Points   (b) Web Buckling

(c) Inadequate width of Bearing Stiffener   (d) Lip Buckling

Figure 49: Failure Modes of Model E

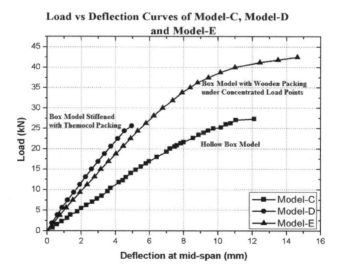

Figure 50: Load Displacement Curves at Mid Span for Model C, D & E

6.3.3 Test results and Discussion of Group-III Models

Having encountered numerous problems with fabrication and connection of group II models and also discouraging structural response in terms of both strength and stiffness of such models, it was concluded that as far as possible complex configurations should be avoided. Accordingly, in addition to simple fabrication as one of the special characteristics, the other important feature of Group III models has been the use of low cost timber planks as innovative stiffening arrangement with a potential to prove very effective against all premature buckling modes of failure. Moreover, codal design rules are also available for such simple CFS sections, thus facilitating reasonable theoretical prediction about load carrying capacity of such sections. This group has three models named as Model F, G and H. The experimental curves of these models for selected tests only are presented in this section. Similar experimental curves of other recorded data are presented in Appendix B.

Figure 51 shows the experimental load v/s displacement curve of Model F at mid span. The curve shows that the model initially responded linearly up to point A followed by slight non-linear response up to point B. At this stage of testing, the model experienced premature localized buckling failure in the lip within the max B M zone and closer to left side applied concentrated load prominently noticeable as seen in Figure 52 (a). The model could resist the maximum load of 70kN with corresponding mid span displacement of 16.08mm. At this stage, the model suddenly stopped resisting any further load, hence rightly called failure load of Model F. This failure was accompanied by slight flange buckling at the same location as seen in Figure 52 (b). It needs to be highlighted here that unlike thermocol packing, the timber planks firmly connected to this model of simplified fabrication has drastically improved the load carrying capacity from 42.5 kN to 70 kN (i.e, Increase by 70%). Except localized lip buckling and mild flange failure confined to very small length, rest of the model apparently seemed in good condition and may have still some reserve strength.

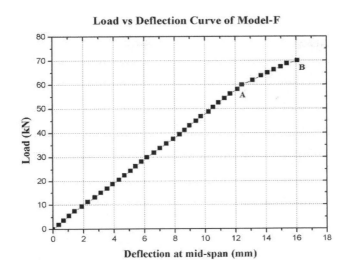

Figure 51: Load Displacement Curve at Mid Span for Model F

(a) Lip Buckling   (b) Flange Buckling

Figure 52: Failure Modes of Model F

To utilize the expected reserved strength, it was deemed appropriate to rectify the model F by strengthening the weakened spot and similar vulnerable locations. Accordingly further loading was stopped and the model was unloaded. After rectifying the localized dent, appropriate strengthening measures were taken by providing lateral intermittent stiffeners at the failure spot and other similar locations. The rectified model was named as Model G.

Figure 53 shows the experimental load deflection curve of the model G. The curve indicates a linear response during initial stage of the loading up to point A. Beyond the elastic linearity, the beam continued to resist the further load confirmed by the rising part of the curve from point A to B

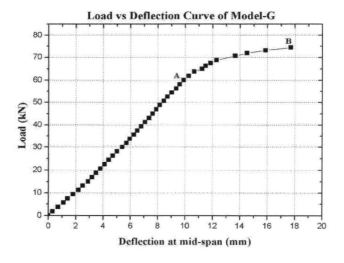

Figure 53: Load Displacement Curve at Mid Span for Model G

This modified model G resisted a maximum load of 74.4 kN against 70 kN resisted by Model F, which was much lower than expected. The pattern of failure observed was again local lip buckling followed by compression flange buckling, both near left support as seen in Figure 54 (a) & (b). It is worth noting here that the load carrying capacity of Model B of Group-I (i.e. simple fabrication with angle stiffeners) and the present Model G are comparable. However the weight/strength ratio of the Model G (i.e. 0.24) is significantly lower than that of Model B (i.e. 0.39), thus proving better steel economy in Model G which is highly desirable.

(a) Lip Buckling   (b) Flange Buckling

Figure 54: Failure Modes of Model G

After noticing promising contribution by timber stiffening in models F and G, it was felt appropriate to investigate how such stiffening arrangement performs for much lighter CFS models. Accordingly, an attempt was made to fabricate Model H of symmetrical I shape using thinner wall thickness i.e. 1.2mm and stiffened with timber planks.

Figure 55 shows the experimental load deflection curve of the model H. The curve shows a linear response during initial loading up to point A. Beyond the point of elastic linearity, the beam continued to resist the further load clearly indicated by the rising trend of the curve from point A to point B in Figure 55. The resistance offered by the beam beyond point A up to B was partly due to reserve capacity of the section and partly due to strain hardening. The model failed at maximum load of 31.25 kN with a deflection of 25.9mm at the centre.

Localized lip buckling failure followed by buckling of compression zone were observed near one of the applied loading points as seen in Figure 56 (a), (b) & (c).

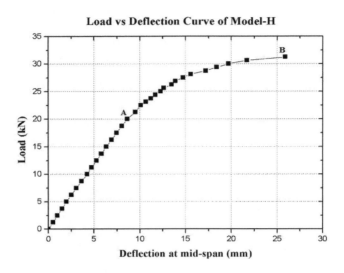

Figure 55: Load Displacement Curve at Mid Span for Model H

(a) Flange Buckling   (b) Lip Buckling

(c) Compression Flange Failure

Figure 56: Failure Modes of Model H

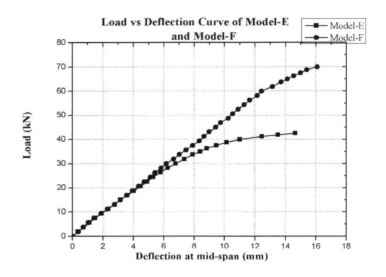

Figure 57: Load Displacement Curve at Mid Span for Model E and G

It is worth mentioning here that use of the timber planks (in place of thermocol adopted for Group-II) as stiffening measure against premature buckling of vulnerable elements of section i.e. compression flange and web has greatly contributed to much improved load carrying capacity i.e. from 42.5kN to 74.4kN (increase by 75%) as is clear from combined plot of two models E and G in Figure 57.

6.3.4   Test results and Discussion of Group-IV Models

One of the primary objectives of using CFS sections is steel economy and this can be successfully achieved by reducing weight for which use of minimum possible wall thickness of sections is the most favourable option. Accordingly, an attempt was made in the present work to adopt only 1mm sheets to fabricate lightest models and explore their structural performance experimentally. Two lightest models named as model I and model J were fabricated under this group.

Figure 58 shows the experimental load v/s displacement curve of Model I at mid span. The curve depicts linear response up-to Point A at which it experienced premature local Lip buckling failure within middle third zone of maximum B M. From A to B the response was nonlinear. It is worth highlighting here that the said failure was prominently noticed as seen in Figure 59 corresponding to very low load of 13kN and mid span displacement of 5.04mm. At this stage, the model suddenly

76

stopped resisting any further load, hence the Model was said to have reached to its limit state. Except localized lip failure confined to very small length, the rest of the model seemed in good condition and expected to possess appreciable reserve strength.

Load vs Deflection Curve of Model-I

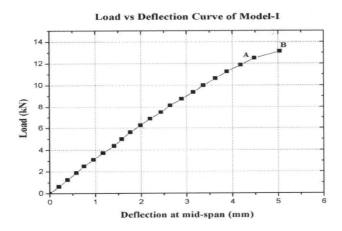

Figure 58: Load Displacement Curve at Mid Span for Model I

Figure 59: Lip Buckling failure of Model I

To exploit its reserve strength, It was felt necessary to strengthen the model with appropriate measures. Accordingly the localized dent in the lip was rectified and lateral intermittent stiffeners in the form of steel strips were introduced to strengthen the entire vulnerable zone of higher B M. The stiffened model was named as model J.

Figure 60 shows the experimental load-displacement curve of Model J at mid span. The curve shows a linear response during initial testing up to point A. Beyond the end of elastic linearity, the beam continued to resist the further small load from point A to point B as seen in Figure 60. The stiffened model also failed at meager load of 15 kN against 13kN resisted by unstiffened model (i.e. only a meager increase of 2kN) as seen in combined plot of the two models in Figure 61. The mode of failure was again local lip buckling within middle third zone of high B M, and is prominently noticeable as seen in Figure 62. At this stage, the model suddenly stopped resisting any further load, hence the Model was said to have reached to its failure.

It is therefore concluded that using very thin sheets, (thickness 1mm or less) for fabrication of CFS beams are highly vulnerable to premature buckling at very low loads even after adopting some stiffening arrangements, hence not recommended.

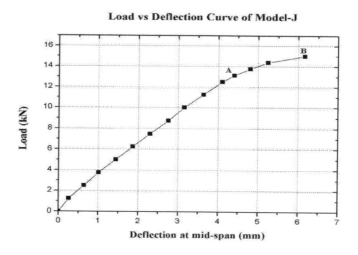

Figure 60: Load Displacement Curve at Mid Span for Model J

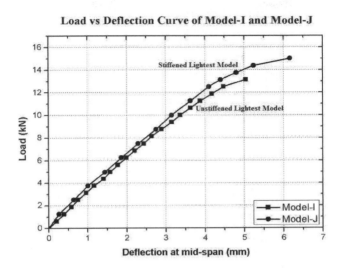

Figure 61: Load Displacement Curve at Mid Span for Model I & J

Figure 62: Lip Buckling failure of Model J

6.3.5 Test results and Discussion of Group-V Model

CFS sections is being considered as one of ideal options to replace the hot rolled section wherever possible to effect steel economy in construction industry, one of the challenging global problems world over. It would be appropriate to have experimental results of a comparable hot rolled section for meaningful comparison with judiciously proposed new CFS sections through innovative techniques.

Accordingly, hot rolled ISMB-150 @ 15kg/m, named Model K, was chosen as the only reference beam model for testing as beam model (having all other conditions identical) to have meaningful comparison with experimental results of various CFS beam models fabricated with innovative techniques.

Figure 63 shows the experimental load v/s mid span displacement curve of Model K. The curve shows a linear response till it experienced lateral buckling as seen in Figure 64 corresponding to failure load of 83.65kN and mid span displacement of 16 mm.

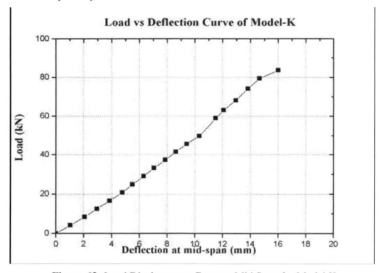

Figure 63: Load Displacement Curve at Mid Span for Model K

Figure 64: Lateral Buckling of hot rolled section ISMB-150

6.4 Overall Comparison of Best Models

Section 6.3 presented the experimental results of various test models under five different groups. In each group, result presentation has been followed by detailed interpretation and necessary discussions supported by relevant photographs. The comparison of test results of various models with specific variations in each group was also made through a combined experimental *load versus vertical mid span displacement* to identify the model/or models in each group with best structural performance. It is also equally important to facilitate such a comparison which would help in identifying the model with best structural performance among the groups. Accordingly, a combined plot of the best model/s identified in each group has been plotted for the purpose described above and the desired plot is shown in Figure 65. It is clear from the Figure 65 that Model G with timber stiffening arrangement and involving simple fabrication has exhibited the best performance among all the models studied in the present work. The load carrying capacity of steel angle stiffened model and the timber stiffened model are comparable. However the strength to weight ratio of the timber stiffened model (i.e. 4.1) is considerably higher than that of steel angle stiffened model (i.e. 2.51), thus validating much better steel economy achieved in timber stiffened model which is highly encouraging. The overall summary of experimental results covering all the eleven test beam models is also given in Table 13

81

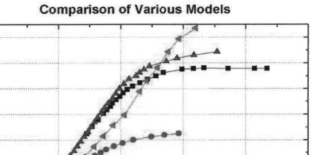

Figure 65: Load Displacement Curves of Best Model from each Group

Models	Weight (kg/m)	Z (10^4 mm^3)	Working Load (kN)	Max load Carried (kN)	Deflection at mid-span (mm)	Strength/ weight	Mode of failure
A	22	6.3	27	42	11.67	1.95	LB
B	27	6.3	27	67.8	21.7	2.51	FB
C	19.8	6.6	28	27.3	15.38	1.38	FB
D	19.8	6.6	28	25.63	4.9	1.29	WB +LB
E	19.8	6.6	28	42.5	14.64	2.14	WB +LB
F	18.44	69	47	70	16.08	3.85	LB + FB
G	18.44	69	47	74.38	17.7	4.1	LB + FB
H	13.77	37.3	28.7	31.25	25.9	2.28	LB + FB
I	10.9	3.15	13.5	13.125	5.04	1.19	LB
J	10.9	3.15	13.5	15	6.16	1.38	LB
K	32.3	1.1	65.7	83.65	16	2.61	Lt.B

Table 13: Summary of all Model Test Results

LB: Lip Buckling
FB: Flange Buckling
WB: Web Buckling
Lt. B: Lateral Buckling

Chapter-7

Conclusions, Recommendations & Future Scope

7.1 Conclusions

Steel on one hand being the only choice as an ideal material for construction of most of the challenging structures, primarily because of its unique structural properties and on other hand it is also the only ideal reinforcing material for concrete to overcome its inherent weakness. Such a reinforcement of concrete has not only transformed it into highly versatile construction material but also enriched it to become the most commonly used construction material as well.

Considering the above enormous importance of steel in the construction industry as well as its limited reserves, there is a pressing need for its most economical utilization. In spite of lacking its potential for achieving the highest economy together with its limited choice of available cross sections, the hot rolled steel members have still been the most popular and widely used steel group in construction industry. However uses of such sections for moderate to lightly loaded structural components (like flooring, roofing systems, etc) generally remain under-utilized thus contributes to considerable wasteful use of such a precious material.

CFS, relatively a new steel group, provides an ideal choice to avoid such a wasteful use of steel. Such a steel group has not only great potential for achieving highest economy, but also permits infinite variety of shapes. Furthermore, structural designers in India are faced with global competition in the design of fast track and cost effective structural systems to meet the huge deficit of various infrastructural systems necessary for bringing the country at par with global standards. For this purpose, CFS sections provide the best choice not only for cost effective structural systems (mentioned above) but also an ideal choice for the high-priority need of fast track construction.

Knowing that the individual components of CFS members are thin with respect to their widths, thus prone to multiple modes of premature buckling when used as compression or flexural members. Avoiding such premature buckling of CFS elements is therefore most challenging problem in CFS construction and needs to be addressed with innovative techniques.

Flexural members are the prime members in most of the structures and the sectional profiles given in the relevant CFS code do not exhaust the variety of sections which may prove structurally much more efficient and highly economical as well. Since shape of beam cross section plays an important role, hence there is an urgent need to develop innovative beam sectional profiles that have inherent resistance to such premature buckling modes thus exhibiting much better structural performance.

Furthermore, judiciously provided appropriate stiffening arrangement also contribute greatly in avoiding such premature buckling modes.

Accordingly, an attempt was made in this project work through extensive experimental work to investigate the proposed innovative techniques, both in terms of shapes as well as judicious stiffening arrangements, appropriate to CFS flexural members for their best structural performance. The prominent results obtained in this study are highlighted as under:

- Lip element of conventional simple I section was observed as most vulnerable and developed premature buckling at a compressive stress level much lower than yield stress. The judiciously provided steel angle stiffener which was welded from inside on both lips over full length of vulnerable zone in the above model has greatly contributed to much improved load carrying capacity from 43kN to 67.8kN (i.e. increase by 40%) and much improved stiffness from 3.7kN/mm to 6.0kN/m (i.e. increase by 60%) as is prominently evident from relevant curves of two models in chapter-6. This encouraging experimental result confirms the important role of judiciously provided stiffening arrangements in improving the structural performance of CFS beam sections.

- A low cost innovative stiffening arrangement against premature buckling was adopted using high density thermocol as packing to fill the hollow space within the proposed innovative box compression flange. However, the said local buckling failure on top face of box compression flange was observed at much lower load thus failed to produce expected results. Minor adjustment in the above inadequate stiffening measure through replacement of softer thermocol by wooden pads locally at vulnerable spots (i.e. under concentrated applied load points) has greatly contributed to much improved load carrying capacity from 25.6kN to 42.5kN (i.e. increase by 66%) which is clear from the curves of relevant models in chapter-6. This encouraging experimental result confirms the importance of proper application of stiffening arrangements in improving the structural performance of CFS beam sections.

- Unlike thermocol packing, the timber planks firmly connected to the conventional cold form lipped I section has drastically improved the load carrying capacity from 42.5 kN to 70 kN (i.e. increase by 64.7%). It is also worth mentioning here that the load carrying capacity of steel angle stiffened model and the timber stiffened model are comparable. However the strength / weight ratio of the timber stiffened model (i.e. 4.17) is considerably higher than that of angle stiffened model (i.e. 2.54), thus proving much better steel economy in timber stiffened model which is highly desirable.

- For the fabrication of models falling under the groups I to III, generally 1.6mm and 2mm thick steel sheets used was the main reason for their higher weight thus defeating the primary objective of using light CFS sections for achieving considerable steel economy. A failed attempt made under group IV models in the present work wherein only 1mm thick sheets (i.e minimum practical thickness) were used to fabricate lightest models together with intermittent stiffeners of 2mm thick covering entire vulnerable zone against the premature buckling modes of failure. Unfotunately, the stiffened model developed premature lip buckling at a very low load of 15kN against 13kN resisted by unstiffened model (i.e. without lateral stiffenrs) before lip buckling. It was concluded that stiffening arrangement produces promising results subjected to the condition that section has adequate wall thickness i.e. not less than 1.5mm.

7.2 Recommendations

Based on the observations and lessons learned during the present study, the following are the proposed recommendations:

- To facilitate desired good quality fabrication and sound connection details, simple configuration of beam cross section should be given the highest priority. This would also significantly reduce cost of fabrication and, fabrication time thus making CFS execution both cost effective as well as fast track construction as desired.
- To achieve the desired results of proposed stiffening arrangement, it must be judiciously selected along with appropriate connection details. Due precautions needs to be taken to ensure proper application of the judiciously chosen stiffening arrangement.
- Selection of appropriate packing or connecting materials along with their proper connection details play important role in achieving much better structural performance, hence must be given due consideration .
- Very thin walled sections, i.e. sheet thickness less or equal to 1mm should not be used in CFS beams to avoid not only inevitable premature local buckling failures at much lower loads but also great difficulties encountered in making the direly needed stiffening arrangement very effective.

7.3 Future Scope

The present study has not only yielded promising results but helped in identifying some of the crucial problems about the CFS flexural members thus necessitating further result oriented investigations, described as under:.

- Since design rules in national/international codes are available only for limited sectional profiles and this being the main reason for limited use of CFS in construction industry. In order to promote the use of CFS sections on a large scale, there is an urgent need to develop generalized design rules covering wide range of CFS sectional profiles (conventional as well as innovative) for safe design of CFS members in general and flexural members in particular. For this purpose a methodical and comprehensive parametric study using advanced analytical techniques like finite element modeling on one hand and high precision experimental investigation on the other hand will be required.

- Since both finite element based parametric study as well as extensive experimental investigation involve painstaking research work and will also be a time consuming activity. Till such design rules become available, it will be appropriate to find suitable modification factors through relevant experimental study necessary for extension of existing design rules to other non conventional sectional profiles.

- The analytical design rules developed for CFS flexural members cannot be used in practice unless thoroughly validated by reliable experimental data. Hence, there is a need to undertake the appropriate experimental validation of all such design rules by simulating the idealized conditions of specific analytical models as closely as possible.

- In real practice, Bending Moment is generally accompanied by Shear Force and may at times be also accompanied by Torsion with significant magnitude. To understand behavior of predominantly flexural members under such combined forces, further study including experimental investigation will be necessary to investigate interaction effects of possible force combinations on development of design rules for such cases.

- The ongoing search for further innovative sectional profiles with potential to have even much better inherent capacity to resist premature buckling modes of failure should continue.

- Development of further innovative lateral stiffening arrangements which are much more effective as well as economical should also be considered.

APPENDIX - A

Design & Analysis of Loading of Group II Models (Model C/ Model D / Model E) according To AS/NZ 4600

Determination of Sectional Properties.

The distance of extreme fiber in compression from neutral axis is

$$\overline{Y} = 74.54 \text{ mm from top}$$

Moment of Inertia of the Section

$$I_{xx} = \left(\frac{150 \times 1.6^3}{12} + 150 \times 1.6 \times 74.54^2\right) + \left(2\left[\frac{1.6 \times 25^3}{12} + 1.6 \times 25 \times 62.04^2\right]\right) +$$
$$\left(2\left[\frac{62.5 \times 1.6^3}{12} + 62.5 \times 1.6 \times 49.54^2\right]\right) + \left(2\left[\frac{1.6 \times 150^3}{12} + 1.6 \times 150 \times (25.46)^2\right]\right) + \left(\left[\frac{100 \times 1.6^3}{12} + 100 \times 1.6 \times (100.46)^2\right]\right) + \left(2\left[\frac{1.6 \times 15^3}{12} + 1.6 \times 15 \times 92.96^2\right]\right)$$

$$\sum I_{xx} = 53.72 \times 10^5 \text{mm}^4$$

Now Sectional Modulus

$$Z_y = \left(\frac{\sum I_{xx}}{\overline{Y}}\right) = \frac{53.72 \times 10^5}{74.54} = 72068.36 \text{mm}^3$$

$$M_y = Z_y \times f_Y = 72064.36 \times 250 = 18.01 \text{KNm}$$

Determination of effective design width

1. $$\lambda = \frac{1.05}{\sqrt{4}}\left(\frac{150}{1.6}\sqrt{\frac{250}{2 \times 10^5}}\right) = 1.74$$

This shows that $\lambda > 0.673$

$$\therefore \quad b_e = \rho b$$

And,

$$\rho = \left(\frac{1 - \frac{0.22}{1.74}}{1.74}\right) = 0.5$$

$$\therefore \quad b_e = 0.5 \times 150 = 75 \text{mm}$$

2. $$\psi = \left(\frac{182.88}{250}\right)$$

$$\psi = 0.73$$

$k = 4+2(1-0.73)^3+2(1-0.73) = 4.68$

$$\lambda = \frac{1.052}{\sqrt{4.68}}\left(\frac{25}{1.6}\sqrt{\frac{250}{2\times10^5}}\right)$$

$\lambda = 0.26$

$\lambda < 0.673$

$b_e = b = 25mm$

3. $$\lambda = \frac{1.05^2}{\sqrt{4}}\left(\frac{62.5}{1.6}\sqrt{\frac{182.88}{2\times10^5}}\right) = 0.62$$

This shows that $\lambda < 0.673$

∴ $b_e = b = 62.5mm$

4. $$\psi = \left(\frac{182.88}{250}\right)$$

$\psi = 0.73$

$k = 4.68$

$$\lambda = \frac{1.052}{\sqrt{4.68}}\left(\frac{150}{1.6}\sqrt{\frac{250}{2\times10^5}}\right) = 1.61$$

$\lambda > 0.673$

$$\gamma = \left(\frac{1-\frac{0.22}{1.61}}{1.61}\right) = 0.54$$

$b_e = 0.54 \times 150 = 80.4mm$

Available b in compression $= 74.54 - 25 = 49.54$ mm

Determination of Modified Sectional Properties

Element	b_e	T	A	$\overline{Y}$	$A\overline{Y}$
1	75	1.6	120	74.54	8944.8
2	25	1.6	40	62.04	2481.6
3	62.5	1.6	100	49.54	4954
4C	49.54	1.6	79.26	24.77	1963.27
4T	100.46	1.6	1600.73	50.23	8073.47
5	100	1.6	160	100.46	16073.6
6	15	1.6	24	92.96	2231.04
			$\sum A=683.99$		$\sum A\overline{Y}=44721.78$

Table 14: Modified Sectional Properties of Group-II Models

Distance to N/A from top

$$Y' = \left(\frac{\Sigma A \bar{Y}}{\Sigma A}\right) = \left(\frac{44721.78}{683.99}\right) = 65.38 \text{mm}$$

Y'= 65.38mm

Determination of reduced Moment of Inertia of the Section

$$\Sigma I_{xx} = \left(\frac{75 \times 1.6^3}{12} + 75 \times 1.6 \times 65.38^2\right) + \left(2\left[\frac{1.6 \times 25^3}{12} + 1.6 \times 25 \times 52.88^2\right]\right) + \left(2\left[\frac{62.5 \times 1.6^3}{12} + 62.5 \times 1.6 \times 40.382 + 21.6 \times 49.54312 + 1.6 \times 49.54 \times 24.772\right.\right. +$$

$$\left(2\left[\frac{1.6 \times 100.46^3}{12} + 1.6 \times 100.46 \times (50.23)^2\right]\right) + \left(\left[\frac{100 \times 1.6^3}{12} + 100 \times 1.6 \times (100.46)^2\right]\right) +$$

$$\left(2\left[\frac{1.6 \times 15^3}{12} + 1.6 \times 15 \times 92.96^2\right]\right)$$

$$\Sigma I_{xx} = 43.11 \times 10^5 \text{mm}^4$$

$$\Sigma I_{xx} = 43.11 \times 10^5 \text{mm}^4$$

$$Z = \left(\frac{\Sigma I_{xx}}{Y'}\right) = \frac{43.11 \times 10^5}{65.38} = 65937.5 \text{mm}^3$$

$$M_s = Z_{ex} \times f_y = 65937.5 \times 150 = 9.89 \text{KNm}$$

For a beam under two point loading, the load carrying capacity (W) is

$$W = \frac{9.89 \times 2}{0.7}$$

$$\boxed{W = 28.2 \text{kN}}$$

Design & Analysis of Loading of Group III Models (Model F/ Model G) According To IS-801

Basic design stress $f = 0.6f_y = 0.6 \times 250 = 150 \text{N/mm}^2$ (for stiffened compression elements)

Determination of effective design width

$$b = \left(\frac{125}{2}\right) = 62.5 \text{ and}, t = 1.6$$

Then we have, $\left(\frac{b}{t}\right) = \left(\frac{62.5}{1.6}\right) = 40.625$

But according to Clause 5.2.1.1 of IS 801-1975

$$\left(\frac{b}{t}\right)_{lim} = (446 / \sqrt{f})$$

$$\left(\frac{b}{t}\right)_{lim} = 446 / \sqrt{150}$$

$$\left(b/t\right)_{\text{lim}} = 36.4 \text{ N/mm}^2$$

As seen above,

$$\left(b/t\right) > \left(b/t\right)_{\text{lim}}$$

Therefore,

$$\left(b/t\right) = \frac{658}{\sqrt{f}}\left(1 - \frac{145}{\left(\frac{b}{t}\right)\sqrt{f}}\right)$$

$$\left(b/t\right) = \frac{658}{\sqrt{150}}\left(1 - \frac{145}{40.625\sqrt{150}}\right)$$

$$\left(b/t\right) = 38.06$$

$$b = 60.09\text{mm}$$

Where, w = width of the flange; t = thickness of the flange & f_y = yield stress.

Design of edge stiffener

According to clause 5.2.2 of I.S. 801-1975

The edge stiffener must have minimum moment of inertia equal to

$$I_{\text{min}} = 1.83t^4 \sqrt{\left[\left(b/t\right)^2 - \left(\frac{27590}{f_y}\right)\right]} > 9.2t^4$$

$$I_{\text{min}} = 1.83 \times 1.6^4 \sqrt{(38.06)^2 - \left(\frac{27590}{250}\right)}$$

$$I_{\text{min}} = 426.5 \text{ mm}^4$$

Now, $9.2 \times t^4 = 60.29$

$$I_{\text{min}} > 9.2 \times t^4$$

Hence it is ok.

When the stiffener lip consists of a simple lip bent at right angle to stiffened element, the required overall depth d_{min} of such lip is

$$d_{\text{min}} = 2.8 \times t \left[\left(b/t\right)^2 - \left(\frac{27590}{f_y}\right)\right]^{1/6}$$

$$d_{\text{min}} = 2.8 \times 2 \left[(38.06)^2 - \left(\frac{27590}{250}\right)\right]^{1/6}$$

$$d_{\text{min}} = 14.7 \approx 15\text{mm}$$

$$d_{min} = 15mm$$

Determination of Sectional Properties

$$I_{xx} = 2\times\left[\left(1.6 \times \frac{25^3}{12}\right) + 1.6 \times 25 \times 87.5^2\right]+ 2\times \left[\left(1.6 \times \frac{15^3}{12}\right) + 1.6 \times 15 \times 92.5^2\right]$$

$$+ \left[2 \times \left(150 \times \frac{1.6^3}{12}\right) + 150 \times 1.6 \times 100^2\right] +\left[1.6 \times \frac{200^3}{12}\right]$$

$$I_{xx} = 68.99 \times 10^5$$

We know that,

$$Z = \left(\frac{I_{xx}}{\overline{Y}}\right)$$

$$Z = \left(\frac{68.99 \times 10^5}{100}\right)$$

$$Z = 68990 \text{ mm}^3$$

Determination of Moment & Load Carrying Capacity

$$M = f\,Z$$

$$M = 150 \times 68990$$

$$M = 10.34 \text{ kNm}$$

Where I_{xx} is the moment of inertia of section horizontal axis passing through centroid of the section.

$\overline{Y}$ is the distance of extreme fiber in compression from neutral axis.

Z is the sectional modulus.

& M is the moment carrying capacity

For a beam under two point loading, the load carrying capacity (W) is

$$W = 29.56 \approx 30kN$$

Design & Analysis of Loading of Group III Models (Model F/ Model G) According To IS-883 (1970)

Determination of Design Coefficients

$$p_1 = \left(\frac{t_\omega}{d}\right)$$

$$p_1 = \left(\frac{25}{200}\right) = 0.125$$

$$q_1 = \left(\frac{t_f}{d}\right)$$

$$q_1 = \left(\frac{25}{150}\right) = 0.167$$

Now,
$$\gamma = p_1^2(6 - 8p_1 + 3p_1^2)(1 - q_1) + q_1$$

$$\gamma = 0.125^2\ (6 - 8{\times}0.125 + 3{\times}\ 0.125^2)\ (1\text{-}0.167) + 0.167$$

$$\gamma = 0.23$$

As we know that,

$$K_4 = 0.8 + 0.8\gamma\left[\left(\frac{D^2+894}{D^2+550}\right) - 1\right]$$

$$K_4 = 0.8 + 0.8 \times 0.23\left[\left(\frac{200^2+894}{200^2+550}\right) - 1\right]$$

$$K_4 = 0.8 + 0.184\left[\left(\frac{40894}{40550}\right) - 1\right]$$

$$K_4 = 0.8$$

Determination of Sectional Properties

$$I_{xx} = \left[\left(\frac{150\times25^3}{12}\right) + 150 \times 25 \times 26.9^2 + \left(\frac{25\times175^3}{12}\right) + 25 \times 175 \times 48.10^2\right]$$

$$I_{xx} = 2.4 \times 10^7\,\text{mm}^4$$

And,

$$z = \left(\frac{I_{xx}}{Y}\right)$$

$$z = \left(\frac{2.4\times10^7}{39.4}\right) = 6.14 \times 10^5\,\text{mm}^3$$

Determination of Moment & Load Carrying Capacity

$$M = fZK_4$$

$$M = 12.3 \times 6.14 \times 10^5 \times 0.8$$

$$M = 6\text{kNm}$$

$$W = \left(\frac{9.45}{0.7}\ \text{x}\ 2\ \right)$$

$$W = 17\text{kN}$$

Therefore, Total Section carrying capacity (Steel + Timber) = 30 + 17

$$\boxed{W= 47 \text{ kN.}}$$

Design & Analysis of Loading of Group III Model (Model H) According To IS-801

Basic design stress $f=0.6f_y=0.6 \times 250=150\text{N/mm}^2$ (for stiffened compression elements)

Determination of effective design width

$$b =\left(\tfrac{150}{2}\right) = 75 \text{and,} t = 1.6$$

Then we have, $\left(b/t\right)= \left(\tfrac{75}{1.6}\right)= 46.875$

But according to Clause 5.2.1.1 of IS 801-1975

$$\left(b/t\right)_{\text{lim}} = \left(446 \ / \ \sqrt{f}\right)$$

$$\left(b/t\right)_{\text{lim}} =\left(446 \ / \ \sqrt{150}\right)$$

$$\left(b/t\right)_{\text{lim}} = 36.4 \text{ N/mm}^2$$

As seen above,

$$b/t > \left(b/t\right)_{\text{lim}}$$

Therefore,

$$b/t = \frac{658}{\sqrt{f}}\left[1 - \left(\frac{145}{\left(\frac{b}{t}\right)\sqrt{f}}\right)\right]$$

$$b/t = \frac{658}{\sqrt{150}}\left[1 - \left(\frac{145}{46.875 \sqrt{150}}\right)\right]$$

$$b = 48.19 \text{ mm}$$

Where, w = width of the flange; t = thickness of the flange & f_y = yield stress.

Design of edge stiffener

According to clause 5.2.2 of I.S. 801-1975

The edge stiffener must have minimum moment of inertia equal to

$$I_{min} = 1.83t^4 \sqrt{\left(b/_t\right)^2 - \left(\frac{27590}{f_y}\right)} > 9.2t^4$$

$$I_{min} = 1.83 \ 1.6^4 \sqrt{(48.19/1.2)^2 - \left(\frac{27590}{250}\right)}$$

$$I_{min} = 143.4 \ mm^4$$

Now,

$$9.2 \times t^4 = 9.2 \times 1.2^4$$

$$9.2 \times t^4 = 19.2$$

$$I_{min} > 9.2 \times t^4$$

Hence it is ok.

When the stiffener lip consists of a simple lip bent at right angel to stiffened element, the required overall depth d_{min} of such lip is

$$d_{min} = 2.8 \times t \left[\left(b/_t\right)^2 - \left(\frac{27590}{fy}\right)\right]^{1/6}$$

$$d_{min} = 2.8 \times t \left[\left(\frac{48.19}{1.2}\right)^2 - \left(\frac{27590}{250}\right)\right]^{1/6}$$

$$d_{min} = 11.27 \approx 15mm$$

$$d_{min} = 15mm$$

Determination of Sectional Properties

$$I_{xx} = 2\left[1.2 \times \frac{25^3}{12} + 1.2 \times 25 \times 62.5^2\right] + 2$$

$$\left[1.2 \times \frac{15^3}{12} + 1.2 \times 15 \times \qquad 67.5^2\right] + 2\left[\left(175 \times \frac{1.2^3}{12}\right) + 175 \times 1.2 \times 75^2\right] + \left[1.2 \times \frac{150^3}{12}\right]$$

$$I_{xx} = 31 \times 10^5 \ mm^4$$

We know that,

$$Z = \left(\frac{I_{xx}}{\bar{Y}}\right)$$

$$Z = \left(\frac{31 \times 10^5}{75}\right)$$

Z = 41333.3 mm³

Determination of Moment & Load carrying capacity

$$M = f Z$$

$$M = 41333.3 \times 150$$

$$M = 6.2 \text{ kNm}$$

Where I_{xx} is the moment of inertia of section horizontal axis passing through centroid of the section.

$\overline{Y}$ is the distance of extreme fiber in compression from neutral axis.

Z is the sectional modulus.

& M is the moment carrying capacity

For a beam under two point loading, the load carrying capacity (W) is

$$W = 17.7 \approx 18 \text{kN}$$

$$W = 18 \text{kN}$$

Design & Analysis of Loading of Group III Model(Model H) According To IS-883 (1970)

Determination of Design Coefficients

$$p_1 = \left(\frac{t_\omega}{d}\right)$$

$$p_1 = \left(\frac{25}{150}\right) = 0.167$$

$$q_1 = \left(\frac{t_f}{d}\right)$$

$$q_1 = \left(\frac{25}{175}\right) = 0.142$$

Now,

$$\gamma = p_1^2(6 - 8p_1 + 3p_1^2)(1 - q_1) + q_1$$

$$\gamma = 0.167^2 (6 - 8 \times 0.167 + 3 \times 0.167^2)(1 - 0.142) + 0.142$$

$$\gamma = 0.256$$

As we know that,

$$K_4 = 0.8 + 0.8\gamma \left[\left(\frac{D^2 + 894}{D^2 + 550} \right) - 1 \right]$$

$$K_4 = 0.8 + 0.8 \times 0.256 \left[\left(\frac{150^2 + 894}{150^2 + 550} \right) - 1 \right]$$

$$K_4 = 0.8 + 0.2[0.15]$$

$$K_4 = 0.8$$

Determination of Sectional Properties

$$I_{xx} =$$
$$\left[\left(\frac{175 \times 25^3}{12} \right) + 175 \times 25 \times 31.25^2 + \left(\frac{25 \times 125^3}{12} \right) + 25 \times 125 \times \qquad 43.75^2 \right]$$

$$= 1.46 \times 10^7$$

We know that,

$$Z = \left(\frac{I_{xx}}{\bar{Y}} \right)$$

$$Z = 332589.2$$

And,

$$M = fzK_4$$

$$= 12.3 \times 332589.2 \times 0.8$$

$$= 3.27 \text{ kNm}$$

$$= 9.35 \approx 9.5 \text{ kN}$$

Therefore, Total Section carrying capacity (Steel + Timber) = 18 + 9.5

$$\boxed{W = 27.5 \text{ kN}}$$

Design and Analysis of Loading Group IV Models (Model-I/ Model-J) According To IS-801

Basic design stress $f = 0.6f_y = 0.6 \times 250 = 150 \text{N/mm}^2$ (for stiffened compression elements)

Determination of effective design width

$$b = \left(\frac{125}{2} \right) = 62.5 \text{and}, t = 1$$

Then we have, $\left(\frac{b}{t}\right) = \left(\frac{62.5}{1}\right) = 62.5$

But according to Clause 5.2.1.1 of IS 801-1975

$$\left(\frac{b}{t}\right)_{lim} = \left(446 / \sqrt{f}\right)$$

$$\left(\frac{b}{t}\right)_{lim} = \left(446 / \sqrt{150}\right)$$

$$\left(\frac{b}{t}\right)_{lim} = 36.4 \text{ N/mm}^2$$

As seen above,

$$\left(\frac{b}{t}\right) > \left(\frac{b}{t}\right)_{lim}$$

Therefore,

$$\left(\frac{b}{t}\right) = \frac{658}{\sqrt{f}}\left(1 - \frac{145}{\left(\frac{b}{t}\right)\sqrt{f}}\right)$$

$$\left(\frac{b}{t}\right) = \frac{658}{\sqrt{150}}\left(1 - \frac{145}{62.5\sqrt{150}}\right)$$

$$b = 43.5 \text{ mm}$$

Where, w = width of the flange; t = thickness of the flange & f_y = yield stress.

Design of edge stiffener

According to clause 5.2.2 of I.S. 801-1975

The edge stiffener must have minimum moment of inertia equal to

$$I_{min} = 1.83t^4 \sqrt{\left(\frac{b}{t}\right)^2 - \left(\frac{27590}{f_y}\right)} > 9.2t^4$$

$$I_{min} = 1.83 \times 1^4 \sqrt{(43.5)^2 - \left(\frac{27590}{250}\right)}$$

$$I_{min} = 75.6 \text{mm}^4$$

Now,

$$9.2t^4 = 9.2$$

$$I_{min} > 9.2 \times t^4$$

Hence it is ok.

When the stiffener lip consists of a simple lip bent at right angle to stiffened element, the required overall depthd_{min} of such lip is

$$d_{min} = 2.8 \times t \left[\left(\frac{b}{t} \right)^2 - \frac{27590}{fy} \right]^{\frac{1}{6}}$$

$$d_{min} = 2.8 \times 2 \left[(43.5)^2 - \frac{27590}{250} \right]^{\frac{1}{6}}$$

$$d_{min} = 9.6 \approx 10mm$$

$$d_{min} = 10 \text{ mm}$$

Determination of Sectional Properties

$$I_{xx} = \left(4 \left[\left(1 \times \frac{25^3}{12} \right) + 1 \times 25 \times 62.5^2 \right] \right) + 2 \left[\left(125 \times \frac{1^3}{12} \right) + 1 \times \right. \quad 125 \times$$
$$752 + 2 \times 150312$$

$$I_{xx} = 2364583$$

We know that,

$$Z = \left(\frac{I_{xx}}{\overline{Y}} \right)$$

$$Z = 31527.77 \text{ mm}^3$$

Determination of Moment & Load carrying capacity

$$M = f Z$$

$$M = 4.729 \text{ kNm}$$

Where $I_{xx}$is themoment of inertia of section horizontal axis passing through centroid of the section.

$\overline{Y}$is the distance of extreme fiber in compression from neutral axis.

Z is the sectional modulus.

& M is the moment carrying capacity

For a beam under two point loading, the load carrying capacity (W) is

$$\boxed{W = 13.5 \text{ kN}}$$

Design and Analysis of Loading Group V Model(Model K) According To IS-800

Sectional Properties from SP-6

$I_z = 718 \times 10^4 \text{mm}^4$

$Z_{pz} = 95.7 \times 10^3 \text{mm}^3$

$Z_{pz} = 110.48 \times 10^3 \text{mm}^3$

Determination of Type of Section

$$\epsilon = \sqrt{\frac{250}{250}} = 1.0$$

$$\left(b/t_f\right) = \left(\frac{75/2}{8}\right) = 4.68 < 9.4\,\epsilon$$

$$d/t_\omega = \left(\frac{(150-2\times8)}{5}\right) = 26.8 < 84\,\epsilon$$

$\therefore$ section is plastic, hence $\beta_b = 1.0$

Determination of Moment & Load carrying capacity

$$L_{LT} = 0.85 \times 1 = 0.85\text{m}$$

$$f_{cr,b} = \sqrt{\left[\frac{1.1\times\pi^2\times2\times10^5}{\left(\frac{0.85\times10^8}{15.7}\right)^2}\right]\left[1 + \frac{1}{50}\left(\frac{850/15.7}{134/8}\right)^2\right]}$$

$$f_{cr,b} = 740.77\,(1.233)$$

$$f_{cr,b} = 914$$

Now,

$$\lambda_{LT} = \sqrt{\frac{250}{914}} = 0.523$$

And,

$$\phi_{LT} = 0.5[1 + 0.21(0.523-0.2)+0.532^2]$$

$$\phi_{LT} = 0.67$$

$$\chi_{LT} = \left(\frac{1}{0.67+\sqrt{[0.67^2-0.523^2]}}\right)$$

$$\chi_{LT} = 0.918$$

99

$$f_{bd} = \left(\frac{x_{LT}\, f_y}{\gamma_{mo}}\right)$$

$$f_{bd} = \left(0.918 \times \frac{250}{1.1}\right) = 208.74$$

Now,
$$M_d = \beta_b Z_\rho f_{bd}$$

$$M_d = 1 \times 110.48 \times 10^3 \times 208.74$$

$$M_d = 23 \text{kNm}$$

For a beam under two point loading, the load carrying capacity (W) is

$$\boxed{W = 63.7 \text{ kN}}$$

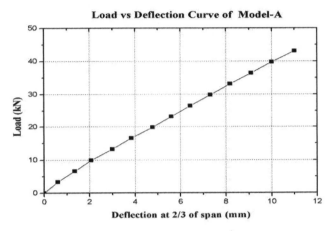

Figure 66: Load Displacement Curve at 2/3rd Span for Model A

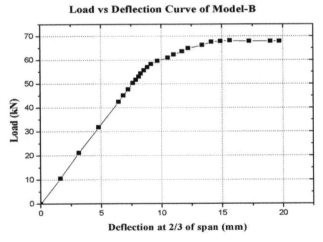

Figure 67: Load Displacement Curve at 2/3rd Span for Model B

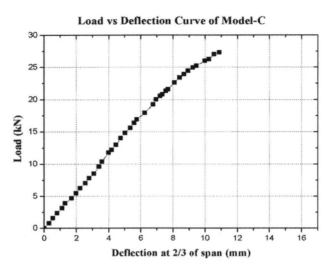

Figure 68: Load Displacement Curve at 2/3rd Span for Model C

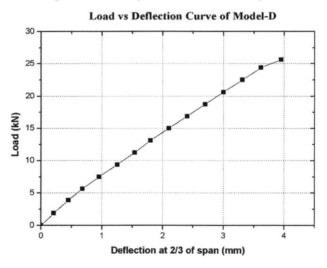

Figure 69: Load Displacement Curve at 2/3rd Span for Model D

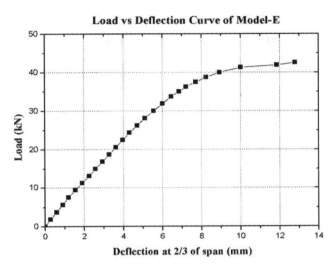

Figure 70: Load Displacement Curve at 2/3rd Span for Model E

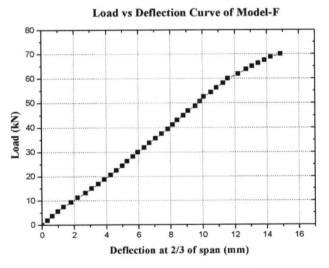

Figure 71: Load Displacement Curve at 2/3rd Span for Model F

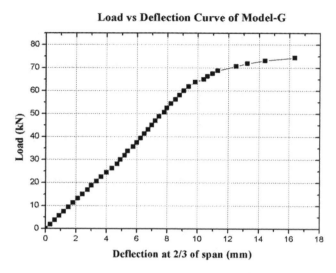

Figure 62: Load Displacement Curve at 2/3rd Span for Model G

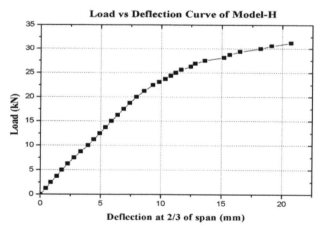

Figure 73: Load Displacement Curve at 2/3rd Span for Model H

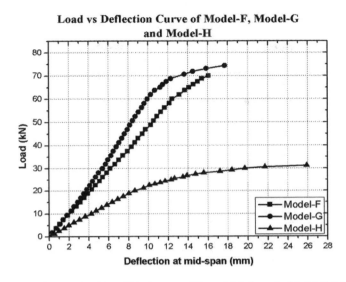

Figure 74: Combined Load Displacement Plot at Mid Span for Model F,G & H

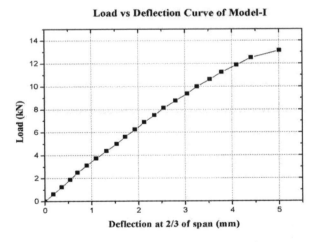

Figure 75: Load Displacement Curve at 2/3rd Span for Model I

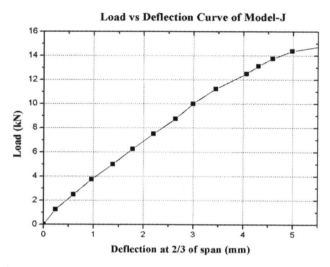

Figure 76: Load Displacement Curve at 2/3rd Span for Model J

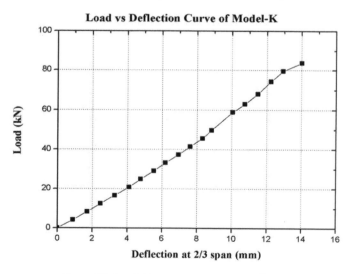

Figure 77: Load Displacement Curve at 2/3rd Span for Model K

REFERENCES

Adil Dar M., Deepankar K. Ashish&Dar A.R. (2014)."A Study on Cold Formed Steel Beams- A Review", *Journal on Structural Engineering*, Vol.3, No.3, pp.34-40

American Iron & Steel Institute, (1991), "Load & Resistance Factor Design specification for Cold Formed Steel Structural Members", Washington

American Iron & Steel Institute, (1996), " Specification for the Design of Cold Formed Steel Structural Members", Washington

Arya A.S. &Ajmani J.L.(2012), Design of Steel Structures, Nemchand Publications, Roorkee

British Standards Institution, (1961), "Specification for the use of Cold Formed Steel Section in Building", PD 4064, Addendum No 1 to BS449, 1959, "The use of Structural Steel in Building"

Canadian Standards Association, (1994), "Cold Formed Steel Structural Members", CAN/CSAS136-94, Rexdale, Ontario

Chajes A., Britvec S.J. & Winter G.(1963), "Effect of Cold Straining on Structural Steel Sheets", *Journal of Structural Division, ASCE Proceedings*,Vol.89,Apr.

Dhalla A.K. & Winter G.(1971), "Ductility Criteria & Performance of Low Ductility Sheets for Cold Formed Members", Proceedings of the First International Specialty Conference on Cold Formed Steel Structures, University of Missouri, Rolla, Missouri, pp. 22-30

Ellifritt D.S., Sputo T. & Haynes J.(1992), "Flexural Capacity of Discretely Braced C's & Z's", *Proceedings Eleventh International Specialty Conference on Cold Formed Steel Structures*, St. Louis.

Eurocode3, (1996), " Design of Steel Structures, part 1.3, General Supplementary Rules for Cold Formed Thin Gauge Members & Sheeting", ENV1993-1-3:1996/AC

Hancock G.J.(1998), "Design of Cold Formed Steel Structures(To AS/NZ4600:1996), 3rd Edition", University of Sydney.

Hancock G.J.(1997), "Design for Distortional Buckling of flexural members", *Thin Walled Structures*, Vol. 27, No. 1, pp. 3-12

IS 800:2007, "Indian Standard, General Construction in Steel, Code of Practice", *Bureau of Indian Standards*, New Delhi. India.

I.S. 801 (1975) Indian Standard Code of Practice for Use of Cold-Formed Light Gauge Steel Structural Members in General Building Construction, *Bureau of Indian Standards*, New Delhi. India.

I.S. 811 (1987) Indian Standard Code of Practice for Cold-Formed Light Gauge Structural Steel Sections, *Bureau of Indian Standards*, New Delhi. India.

IS 883:1970, "Indian Standard Code of Practice for Design of Structural Timber in Building", *Bureau of Indian Standards*, New Delhi. India.

IS 1608:2005, "Metallic Materials – Tensile Testing at Ambient Temperature", *Bureau of Indian Standards*, New Delhi. India.

Karren K.W. & Winter G.(1967), "Effects of Cold Forming on Light Gauge Steel Members", *Journal of Structural Division, ASCE Proceedings*, Vol.93(ST1)

Mcdonald M., Taylor G.T. & Rhodes J.(1997), "The Effect of Cold Forming on the yield strength of thin gauge Steel Hardness test approach", *Thin Walled Structures*, Vol. 29, No. 1-4, pp. 243-256

M.S.Deepak, R.Kandasamy, R. Thenmozhi(2012), "Investigation on Lateral Torsional Buckling Performance of Cold Formed Steel C Channel Sections*", International Journal of Emerging Trends in Engineering & Development*, Issue 2, Volume 4

O Connor C., Goldsmith P.R. &Ryall T.J.(1965), "The Reinforcement of Steel Beams to improve Beam Buckling Strength", *Civil Engineering Transaction*, Institute of Engineers Australia

Pi Y.L. &Trahair N.S.(1997), "Lateral Distortional Buckling of Hollow Flange Beams", *Journal of Structural Engineering , ASCE*, Vol. 123
Standard Association of Australia, (1968), "SAA Steel Structures Code", ASCA1-1968

Standard Association of Australia, (1974), "SAA Cold Formed Steel Structures Code", AS 1538-1974

Standards of Australia, (1996), "Cold Formed Steel Structures", AS/NZ 4600

Steel Construction Institute(1998), "Structural Steel Design", Cambridge, London, UK

Standards of Australia, (1998), "Steel Structures", AS 4100

Winter G.(1970), "Commentary on the 1968 Edition of the specification for the Design of Cold Formed Steel Structural Members", American Iron & Steel Institute, New York

Wu S., Yu W.W. &LaBoube R.A. (1995), "Strength of Flexural Members using Structural Grade 80 of A653 & Grade E of A611 Sheets", First Progress Report, Civil Engineering Study 95-5, University of Missouri, Rolla, Missouri

Zhao &Mahendran M.(2001), "Behavior & Design of Cold Formed Steel Hollow Beam Flange Sections ", PhD Thesis, School of Engineering, Queensland University of Technology, Brisbane, Australia